WORDLY WISE 3000™ Book 7
Test Booklet

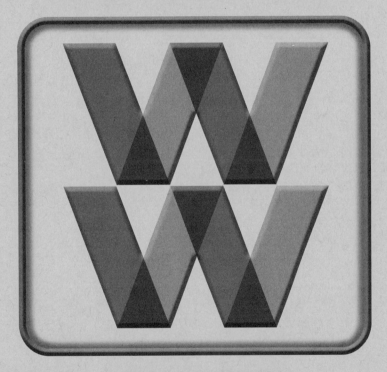

SECOND EDITION

EDUCATORS PUBLISHING SERVICE
Cambridge and Toronto

Printed in U.S.A.

ISBN 978-0-8388-2937-0

2 3 4 5 MLY 11 10 09 08 07

Book 7, Lesson 1 Test

Choose the BEST way to complete each sentence or answer each question. Then fill in the circle next to your answer.

1. A <u>trek</u> is a long, difficult

    Ⓐ   journey.
    Ⓑ   discussion.
    Ⓒ   test.
    Ⓓ   project.

2. When rain <u>abates</u>, it

    Ⓐ   freezes.
    Ⓑ   begins to stop.
    Ⓒ   causes floods.
    Ⓓ   pours down steadily.

3. An <u>agent</u> is someone who

    Ⓐ   works in a restaurant.
    Ⓑ   acts in movies.
    Ⓒ   does business for others.
    Ⓓ   has very good manners.

4. The <u>authorities</u> include

    Ⓐ   all citizens.
    Ⓑ   police officers.
    Ⓒ   pet owners.
    Ⓓ   store owners.

5. An <u>epidemic</u> disease

    Ⓐ   has no cure.
    Ⓑ   is limited to children.
    Ⓒ   is not serious.
    Ⓓ   spreads rapidly.

6. An <u>estimate</u> is

    Ⓐ   a careful guess.

    Ⓑ   a large amount of money.

    Ⓒ   a person's weight.

    Ⓓ   a person's height.

7. To <u>acknowledge</u> a rule is to

    Ⓐ   create it.

    Ⓑ   admit that it exists.

    Ⓒ   reveal it to others.

    Ⓓ   enforce it.

8. To <u>evict</u> someone from an apartment is to

    Ⓐ   force him or her to move out.

    Ⓑ   rent the apartment to him or her.

    Ⓒ   buy the apartment from him or her.

    Ⓓ   furnish the apartment for him or her.

9. Jack's comment is <u>irrelevant</u> to our discussion. His comment

    Ⓐ   may cause an argument.

    Ⓑ   will bring our discussion to an end.

    Ⓒ   adds interest to our discussion.

    Ⓓ   has nothing to do with our discussion.

10. Which describes a <u>sham</u>?

    Ⓐ   visiting a doctor

    Ⓑ   pretending to be sick

    Ⓒ   having a serious illness

    Ⓓ   hoping a sick friend will get well soon

11. Which is a cleaning <u>agent</u>?

    Ⓐ   cleaning powder

    Ⓑ   a dirty home

    Ⓒ   a spotless home

    Ⓓ   someone who prefers cleanliness

12. Which describes an _epidemic_?

    Ⓐ   thousands of people sick with the flu

    Ⓑ   three family members with colds

    Ⓒ   scientists developing new medications

    Ⓓ   a medication that relieves flu symptoms

13. Which is most likely to be _devastating_?

    Ⓐ   a light snowfall

    Ⓑ   a flood

    Ⓒ   overcast skies

    Ⓓ   spring weather

14. Who has the most _authority_ in a school?

    Ⓐ   the principal

    Ⓑ   students

    Ⓒ   cafeteria employees

    Ⓓ   the kindergarten teacher

15. How might you _acknowledge_ a gift?

    Ⓐ   by tearing off the wrapping paper

    Ⓑ   by writing a thank-you note

    Ⓒ   by delivering it to someone's home

    Ⓓ   by wrapping it very carefully

Find a SYNONYM for each underlined word. Then fill in the circle next to your answer.

16. _impartial_

    Ⓐ   careful

    Ⓑ   generous

    Ⓒ   intelligent

    Ⓓ   fair

17. _acknowledged_

    Ⓐ   skilled

    Ⓑ   recognized

    Ⓒ   available

    Ⓓ   fascinating

18. <u>authority</u>

Ⓐ businessperson

Ⓑ student

Ⓒ store owner

Ⓓ expert

19. <u>devastation</u>

Ⓐ melancholy

Ⓑ evil

Ⓒ destruction

Ⓓ fury

20. <u>estimated</u>

Ⓐ knew

Ⓑ hoped

Ⓒ wondered

Ⓓ figured

21. <u>infuriated</u>

Ⓐ angered

Ⓑ implored

Ⓒ saddened

Ⓓ influenced

22. <u>precision</u>

Ⓐ decision

Ⓑ estimation

Ⓒ exactness

Ⓓ education

23. <u>shammed</u>

Ⓐ joked

Ⓑ schemed

Ⓒ pretended

Ⓓ concealed

24. <u>trekked</u>

     Ⓐ performed

     Ⓑ proved

     Ⓒ fought

     Ⓓ traveled

Find an ANTONYM for each underlined word. Then fill in the circle next to your answer.

25. <u>devastate</u>

     Ⓐ group

     Ⓑ repair

     Ⓒ examine

     Ⓓ discuss

26. <u>unabated</u>

     Ⓐ heavy

     Ⓑ generous

     Ⓒ decreasing

     Ⓓ moderate

27. <u>industrious</u>

     Ⓐ cozy

     Ⓑ sunny

     Ⓒ contented

     Ⓓ lazy

28. <u>precise</u>

     Ⓐ distasteful

     Ⓑ unkind

     Ⓒ uncomfortable

     Ⓓ inaccurate

29. <u>sham</u>

     Ⓐ exquisite

     Ⓑ genuine

     Ⓒ silky

     Ⓓ expensive

Book 7, Lesson 2 Test

Choose the BEST way to complete each sentence or answer each question. Then fill in the circle next to your answer.

1. A <u>predator</u> is a person who

   Ⓐ   works as a police officer.
   Ⓑ   works in a restaurant.
   Ⓒ   lives by robbing others.
   Ⓓ   owns a store.

2. To check an object's <u>authenticity</u> is to find out whether it is

   Ⓐ   genuine.
   Ⓑ   heavy enough.
   Ⓒ   working correctly.
   Ⓓ   paid for.

3. To <u>devour</u> a book is to

   Ⓐ   read it to someone.
   Ⓑ   read it quickly and eagerly.
   Ⓒ   search for it in a library.
   Ⓓ   think it is badly written.

4. A <u>predatory</u> animal is one that

   Ⓐ   eats plants.
   Ⓑ   lives on land.
   Ⓒ   kills and eats other animals.
   Ⓓ   lives in the ocean.

5. To <u>slaughter</u> seals is to

   Ⓐ   kill large numbers of them.
   Ⓑ   trap them in a net.
   Ⓒ   put them in zoos.
   Ⓓ   value them for their fur.

6. Mr. Beatty has a <u>prior</u> claim on this property. His claim

    Ⓐ   was established before other people's claims were.

    Ⓑ   is unjustified.

    Ⓒ   is illegal.

    Ⓓ   is under investigation.

7. Which describes a <u>scavenger's</u> behavior?

    Ⓐ   eating an expensive meal in a restaurant

    Ⓑ   setting up a relief center for homeless people

    Ⓒ   planning ways to rebuild damaged buildings

    Ⓓ   searching through a junk heap for usable items

8. Who shows <u>delicacy</u>?

    Ⓐ   Akira, who avoids embarrassing others

    Ⓑ   Ben, who starts arguments

    Ⓒ   Monica, who helps children with their homework

    Ⓓ   Zev, who eats with his elbows on the table

9. Which might someone need to <u>authenticate</u>?

    Ⓐ   a garden

    Ⓑ   a ceiling

    Ⓒ   a storage shed

    Ⓓ   a birth certificate

10. Which describes <u>slaughter</u>?

    Ⓐ   farming and ranching

    Ⓑ   raising pigs, cows, and horses

    Ⓒ   killing animals for food

    Ⓓ   rounding up cattle

11. When would you be most likely to eat a <u>delicacy</u>?

    Ⓐ   at a fancy party

    Ⓑ   every day for lunch

    Ⓒ   at the airport

    Ⓓ   at a hospital

12. Which creature is a <u>scavenger</u>?

    Ⓐ   one that changes color when winter comes

    Ⓑ   one that kills other animals for meat

    Ⓒ   one that eats dead or decaying matter

    Ⓓ   one that eats grasses and leaves

13. "The <u>slaughter</u> on our nation's highways" means

    Ⓐ   the high amounts of traffic during rush hour.

    Ⓑ   the traffic violators on our highways.

    Ⓒ   the many deaths that car accidents cause.

    Ⓓ   the many laws against drunk driving.

Find a SYNONYM for each underlined word. Then fill in the circle next to your answer.

14. <u>authentic</u>

    Ⓐ   emotional

    Ⓑ   true

    Ⓒ   colorful

    Ⓓ   sentimental

15. <u>astute</u>

    Ⓐ   sturdy

    Ⓑ   fearful

    Ⓒ   wise

    Ⓓ   social

16. <u>devoured</u>

    Ⓐ   caught

    Ⓑ   desired

    Ⓒ   sipped

    Ⓓ   ate

17. <u>plumage</u>

    Ⓐ   fur

    Ⓑ   scales

    Ⓒ   feathers

    Ⓓ   skin

18. slaughtered

    Ⓐ herded

    Ⓑ purchased

    Ⓒ ate

    Ⓓ killed

Find an ANTONYM for each underlined word. Then fill in the circle next to your answer.

19. solitude

    Ⓐ recklessness

    Ⓑ companionship

    Ⓒ intelligence

    Ⓓ willingness

20. ungainly

    Ⓐ generous

    Ⓑ smooth

    Ⓒ graceful

    Ⓓ polite

21. vulnerable

    Ⓐ forgiving

    Ⓑ joyful

    Ⓒ calm

    Ⓓ protected

22. predator

    Ⓐ victor

    Ⓑ prey

    Ⓒ enemy

    Ⓓ companion

23. derogatory

    Ⓐ welcoming

    Ⓑ thrifty

    Ⓒ complimentary

    Ⓓ generous

Find the words that correctly complete each analogy. Then fill in the circle next to your answer.

24. prior : later ::

    Ⓐ   wider : narrower

    Ⓑ   wider : thicker

    Ⓒ   wider : taller

    Ⓓ   wider : heavier

25. thief : predatory ::

    Ⓐ   guard : armed

    Ⓑ   guard : protective

    Ⓒ   guard : radio

    Ⓓ   guard : robbery

26. scavenge : search ::

    Ⓐ   purchase : buy

    Ⓑ   purchase : eat

    Ⓒ   purchase : return

    Ⓓ   purchase : store

27. mythical : real ::

    Ⓐ   fascinating : boring

    Ⓑ   fascinating : story

    Ⓒ   fascinating : entertaining

    Ⓓ   fascinating : interesting

28. figment : imaginary ::

    Ⓐ   fact : fiction

    Ⓑ   fact : uncertain

    Ⓒ   fact : real

    Ⓓ   fact : reported

Book 7, Lesson 3 Test

Choose the BEST way to complete each sentence or answer each question. Then fill in the circle next to your answer.

1. Someone who is <u>devoid</u> of fear is

    Ⓐ paralyzed by fear.

    Ⓑ slightly nervous.

    Ⓒ not afraid at all.

    Ⓓ frightening.

2. To <u>heed</u> a warning is to

    Ⓐ laugh at it.

    Ⓑ warn others.

    Ⓒ pay attention to it.

    Ⓓ post a warning sign.

3. Emma was in <u>mortal</u> danger. This means that she

    Ⓐ might have been in danger.

    Ⓑ was in terrible danger.

    Ⓒ narrowly escaped danger.

    Ⓓ was perfectly safe.

4. According to a Greek myth, Hercules was born a god but was raised among <u>mortals</u>. A <u>mortal</u> is a

    Ⓐ superhero.

    Ⓑ monster.

    Ⓒ talking animal.

    Ⓓ human being.

5. <u>Mortal</u> beings are

    Ⓐ godlike.

    Ⓑ animals.

    Ⓒ human.

    Ⓓ killers.

6. To <u>bestow</u> a prize on someone is to

    Ⓐ   steal a prize from that person.

    Ⓑ   honor that person with a prize.

    Ⓒ   race against that person and win.

    Ⓓ   receive a prize from that person.

7. To be <u>heedless</u> of instructions is to

    Ⓐ   explain instructions carefully.

    Ⓑ   try to follow instructions.

    Ⓒ   fail to pay attention to instructions.

    Ⓓ   fail to understand instructions.

8. To <u>muse</u> is to

    Ⓐ   worry constantly.

    Ⓑ   sleep without dreaming.

    Ⓒ   try desperately to think of a plan.

    Ⓓ   think quietly and carefully.

9. Apple Computers <u>pioneered</u> personal computing. This means that Apple

    Ⓐ   opened the way for others.

    Ⓑ   traveled all over the world.

    Ⓒ   began in the 1800s.

    Ⓓ   kept its computers hidden.

10. The applause <u>subsided</u>. It

    Ⓐ   grew more lively.

    Ⓑ   sounded like the ocean.

    Ⓒ   grew more rhythmic.

    Ⓓ   grew quieter.

11. A <u>plague</u> is anything that causes

    Ⓐ   enemies to become friends.

    Ⓑ   destruction or suffering.

    Ⓒ   inconvenience.

    Ⓓ   confusion.

12. In the 1300s, the <u>plague</u> killed about one-third of all Europeans. This means that they died

    Ⓐ   of a disease.

    Ⓑ   in a terrible war.

    Ⓒ   of hunger.

    Ⓓ   of old age.

13. Dr. Martin Luther King Jr. was a <u>pioneer</u> in the Civil Rights movement. This means that he

    Ⓐ   opened the way for others to follow.

    Ⓑ   was a minister's assistant.

    Ⓒ   entered the Civil Rights Movement when it was almost over.

    Ⓓ   traveled around the country.

14. Which is a <u>benefactor</u>?

    Ⓐ   a grocery store shopper

    Ⓑ   a girl who receives money for her birthday

    Ⓒ   a boy who buys his own bicycle

    Ⓓ   a woman who donates $500 to a school

15. Which is an <u>admonition</u>?

    Ⓐ   "Don't speak to strangers!"

    Ⓑ   "What a beautiful day!"

    Ⓒ   "Hello. How are you?"

    Ⓓ   "May I help you carry your groceries?"

Find a SYNONYM for each underlined word. Then fill in the circle next to your answer.

16. <u>wrathful</u>

    Ⓐ   sorrowful

    Ⓑ   exhausted

    Ⓒ   furious

    Ⓓ   devastated

17. <u>admonished</u>

    Ⓐ   explained

    Ⓑ   warned

    Ⓒ   inquired

    Ⓓ   begged

18. aghast

    Ⓐ   sleepy

    Ⓑ   fascinated

    Ⓒ   irritated

    Ⓓ   shocked

19. annihilated

    Ⓐ   attacked

    Ⓑ   destroyed

    Ⓒ   approached

    Ⓓ   explored

20. devious

    Ⓐ   sneaky

    Ⓑ   artificial

    Ⓒ   distasteful

    Ⓓ   sentimental

21. plagued

    Ⓐ   excited

    Ⓑ   infuriated

    Ⓒ   distressed

    Ⓓ   questioned

22. wrath

    Ⓐ   sorrow

    Ⓑ   courage

    Ⓒ   strength

    Ⓓ   fury

23. mortal

    Ⓐ   deep

    Ⓑ   fatal

    Ⓒ   deft

    Ⓓ   vicious

24. heed

    Ⓐ trace

    Ⓑ money

    Ⓒ compliments

    Ⓓ attention

Find an ANTONYM for each underlined word. Then fill in the circle next to your answer.

25. subsided

    Ⓐ splashed

    Ⓑ churned

    Ⓒ foamed

    Ⓓ rose

26. admonished

    Ⓐ greeted

    Ⓑ described

    Ⓒ praised

    Ⓓ organized

27. devious

    Ⓐ rocky

    Ⓑ muddy

    Ⓒ paved

    Ⓓ straight

28. heedful

    Ⓐ lazy

    Ⓑ inattentive

    Ⓒ mischievous

    Ⓓ impolite

29. unwitting

    Ⓐ courageous

    Ⓑ generous

    Ⓒ intentional

    Ⓓ trustworthy

Book 7, Lesson 4 Test

Choose the BEST way to complete each sentence or answer each question. Then fill in the circle next to your answer.

1. If two fingerprints <u>correspond</u>, they

   Ⓐ come from members of the same family.

   Ⓑ match.

   Ⓒ are smeared.

   Ⓓ are similar, but not identical.

2. To <u>inherit</u> money is to

   Ⓐ save it.

   Ⓑ earn it.

   Ⓒ receive it from someone who has died.

   Ⓓ give it to workers who have earned it.

3. <u>Renovation</u> on the building will begin next week. Next week workers will begin

   Ⓐ making the building look like new.

   Ⓑ tearing the building down.

   Ⓒ moving furniture into the building.

   Ⓓ making plans for a brand-new building.

4. Little children require constant <u>supervision</u>. This means that adults must

   Ⓐ give them lots of freedom.

   Ⓑ watch and direct them.

   Ⓒ give them art supplies.

   Ⓓ teach them to read.

5. The computer club <u>comprises</u> 57 members. This means that the club

   Ⓐ consists of 57 members.

   Ⓑ has lost 57 members.

   Ⓒ needs 57 more members.

   Ⓓ has given awards to 57 members.

6. The city's <u>latitude</u> is 110 degrees north. This means that the city is located

    Ⓐ   110 degrees south of the equator.

    Ⓑ   110 degrees north of the equator.

    Ⓒ   110 degrees west of the international date line.

    Ⓓ   110 degrees east of the international date line.

7. To <u>maintain</u> someone's guilt is to

    Ⓐ   declare that that person is innocent.

    Ⓑ   declare that that person is guilty.

    Ⓒ   wonder whether that person is guilty.

    Ⓓ   keep that person's guilt a secret.

8. If someone <u>maintains</u> a certain weight, he or she

    Ⓐ   loses several pounds.

    Ⓑ   neither loses nor gains weight.

    Ⓒ   gains several pounds.

    Ⓓ   prefers a lighter or heavier weight.

9. To <u>maintain</u> a building is to

    Ⓐ   build it.

    Ⓑ   live in it.

    Ⓒ   keep it in good repair.

    Ⓓ   find out if it is for sale.

10. Which describes a <u>correspondence</u>?

    Ⓐ   paintings by a certain artist

    Ⓑ   letters that two people have written to each other

    Ⓒ   books by a certain author

    Ⓓ   songs that a certain musician usually performs

11. Which is an example of <u>competence</u>?

    Ⓐ   a rainy day

    Ⓑ   a delicious meal

    Ⓒ   a runner's ability to win races

    Ⓓ   viewers' enjoyment of a funny movie

12. Which is an <u>acquisition</u>?

    Ⓐ   book that someone has just bought

    Ⓑ   sunny day following a week of rain

    Ⓒ   race with many competitors

    Ⓓ   trial with a judge and jury

13. To <u>correspond</u> with someone is to

    Ⓐ   argue with that person.

    Ⓑ   play games with that person.

    Ⓒ   borrow that person's possessions.

    Ⓓ   exchange letters with that person.

14. To <u>inherit</u> brown eyes is to

    Ⓐ   think brown eyes are beautiful.

    Ⓑ   wish you had brown eyes.

    Ⓒ   have brown eyes because one or both of your parents have them.

    Ⓓ   have brown eyes because one or all of your children have them.

15. Countries in southern <u>latitudes</u> are

    Ⓐ   located a few miles from the South Pole.

    Ⓑ   in North America.

    Ⓒ   north of the equator.

    Ⓓ   south of the equator.

Find a SYNONYM for each underlined word. Then fill in the circle next to your answer.

16. <u>acquire</u>

    Ⓐ   prepare

    Ⓑ   donate

    Ⓒ   obtain

    Ⓓ   accuse

17. <u>competent</u>

    Ⓐ   cheerful

    Ⓑ   willing

    Ⓒ   polite

    Ⓓ   skilled

18. comprised

Ⓐ explained

Ⓑ formed

Ⓒ won

Ⓓ divided

19. dilapidated

Ⓐ disorganized

Ⓑ lazy

Ⓒ pale

Ⓓ shabby

20. incident

Ⓐ home

Ⓑ message

Ⓒ event

Ⓓ accident

21. reprimand

Ⓐ instruction

Ⓑ scolding

Ⓒ exclamation

Ⓓ suggestion

22. supervisor

Ⓐ inspector

Ⓑ parent

Ⓒ director

Ⓓ assistant

23. renovated

Ⓐ remodeled

Ⓑ planned

Ⓒ explored

Ⓓ inspected

24. loath

    Ⓐ   sick

    Ⓑ   reluctant

    Ⓒ   mischievous

    Ⓓ   fearful

25. supervised

    Ⓐ   managed

    Ⓑ   pointed

    Ⓒ   inquired

    Ⓓ   explained

Find an ANTONYM for each underlined word. Then fill in the circle next to your answer.

26. antagonize

    Ⓐ   control

    Ⓑ   communicate

    Ⓒ   befriend

    Ⓓ   supervise

27. illustrious

    Ⓐ   unwitting

    Ⓑ   unattractive

    Ⓒ   unknown

    Ⓓ   outstanding

28. latitude

    Ⓐ   deviousness

    Ⓑ   strictness

    Ⓒ   malice

    Ⓓ   melancholy

29. reprimanded

    Ⓐ   ignored

    Ⓑ   trained

    Ⓒ   directed

    Ⓓ   praised

Book 7, Lesson 5 Test

Choose the BEST way to complete each sentence or answer each question. Then fill in the circle next to your answer.

1. To <u>administer</u> first aid is to

   Ⓐ   treat someone using first aid.

   Ⓑ   teach someone first-aid techniques.

   Ⓒ   read a brochure about first aid.

   Ⓓ   create a poster showing safety rules.

2. To <u>agitate</u> water is to

   Ⓐ   freeze it.

   Ⓑ   drink it.

   Ⓒ   stir it slowly.

   Ⓓ   churn it violently.

3. <u>Citrus</u> fruits include

   Ⓐ   apples and bananas.

   Ⓑ   peaches, pears, and plums.

   Ⓒ   oranges, lemons, and limes.

   Ⓓ   blackberries and blueberries.

4. A student is most likely to <u>disrupt</u> the class by

   Ⓐ   completing an assignment.

   Ⓑ   participating in a class discussion.

   Ⓒ   talking out of turn.

   Ⓓ   staying in during recess.

5. <u>Indifferent</u> health is

   Ⓐ   neither very poor nor excellent.

   Ⓑ   excellent.

   Ⓒ   very poor.

   Ⓓ   very good.

6. To <u>toil</u> up a mountain is to

    Ⓐ   climb it safely.

    Ⓑ   climb it with difficulty.

    Ⓒ   drive to the top.

    Ⓓ   cycle to the top.

7. Which is an <u>urgent</u> message?

    Ⓐ   "You have a dentist appointment tomorrow at four o'clock."

    Ⓑ   "Please call home right away!"

    Ⓒ   "I hope you can come to my party on Saturday."

    Ⓓ   "We are almost out of milk. Please buy some."

8. Which is most <u>strenuous</u>?

    Ⓐ   carrying heavy trash cans

    Ⓑ   typing on a computer keyboard

    Ⓒ   taking a stroll

    Ⓓ   playing catch

9. She had no choice but to accept a <u>menial</u> job. Her job was

    Ⓐ   interesting and rewarding.

    Ⓑ   exciting and fun-filled.

    Ⓒ   boring but not difficult.

    Ⓓ   low-level and poorly paid.

10. How can people fight <u>illiteracy</u>?

    Ⓐ   by avoiding arguments with others

    Ⓑ   by teaching others to read and write

    Ⓒ   by visiting a doctor for regular check-ups

    Ⓓ   by getting plenty of exercise

11. Where could you find <u>citrus</u> fruit?

    Ⓐ   on orange trees

    Ⓑ   in a bowl of apples

    Ⓒ   on oak trees

    Ⓓ   in a glass of tomato juice

12. To <u>agitate</u> for new laws is to

    Ⓐ   stir up support for them.

    Ⓑ   pass them.

    Ⓒ   oppose them.

    Ⓓ   decide whether they are fair.

Find a SYNONYM for each underlined word. Then fill in the circle next to your answer.

13. <u>disruption</u>

    Ⓐ   disturbance

    Ⓑ   dishonor

    Ⓒ   distrust

    Ⓓ   distinction

14. <u>administer</u>

    Ⓐ   preach

    Ⓑ   explain

    Ⓒ   teach

    Ⓓ   manage

15. <u>capitulated</u>

    Ⓐ   battled

    Ⓑ   escaped

    Ⓒ   surrendered

    Ⓓ   pleaded

16. <u>disrupt</u>

    Ⓐ   interrupt

    Ⓑ   command

    Ⓒ   control

    Ⓓ   organize

17. <u>respite</u>

    Ⓐ   refreshment

    Ⓑ   enjoyment

    Ⓒ   pause

    Ⓓ   amusement

18. strenuous

    Ⓐ vigorous

    Ⓑ curious

    Ⓒ generous

    Ⓓ reasonable

19. toil

    Ⓐ difficulty

    Ⓑ exhaustion

    Ⓒ labor

    Ⓓ worker

Find an ANTONYM for each underlined word. Then fill in the circle next to your answer.

20. adequate

    Ⓐ rough

    Ⓑ plain

    Ⓒ unattractive

    Ⓓ insufficient

21. agitated

    Ⓐ renovated

    Ⓑ amused

    Ⓒ interested

    Ⓓ soothed

22. disruptive

    Ⓐ kind

    Ⓑ cooperative

    Ⓒ generous

    Ⓓ intelligent

23. hovel

    Ⓐ shed

    Ⓑ home

    Ⓒ mansion

    Ⓓ building

24. indifferent

    Ⓐ intelligent

    Ⓑ educated

    Ⓒ reasonable

    Ⓓ concerned

25. permanent

    Ⓐ temporary

    Ⓑ dilapidated

    Ⓒ devastated

    Ⓓ distressed

Find the words that correctly complete each analogy. Then fill in the circle next to your answer.

26. lemon : citrus ::

    Ⓐ spaghetti : thin

    Ⓑ spaghetti : pasta

    Ⓒ spaghetti : restaurant

    Ⓓ spaghetti : meatball

27. illiterate : books ::

    Ⓐ deaf : poetry

    Ⓑ deaf : warmth

    Ⓒ deaf : food

    Ⓓ deaf : music

28. work : toil ::

    Ⓐ eat : predator

    Ⓑ eat : devour

    Ⓒ eat : lion

    Ⓓ eat : drink

29. urgency : action ::

    Ⓐ exhaustion : heat

    Ⓑ exhaustion : effort

    Ⓒ exhaustion : rest

    Ⓓ exhaustion : tired

Book 7, Lesson 6 Test

Choose the BEST way to complete each sentence or answer each question. Then fill in the circle next to your answer.

1. An <u>addict</u> has a strong desire

   Ⓐ   to get a good education.
   Ⓑ   for a habit-forming substance.
   Ⓒ   for success.
   Ⓓ   for a family.

2. To <u>confront</u> someone with a crime is to

   Ⓐ   wonder about that person's honesty.
   Ⓑ   forgive that person.
   Ⓒ   steal from that person.
   Ⓓ   accuse that person.

3. When a television show <u>debuts</u>,

   Ⓐ   actors audition for it.
   Ⓑ   it is shown for the first time.
   Ⓒ   it comes back for a second season.
   Ⓓ   it goes off the air.

4. A <u>blatant</u> attempt to sell products to children is

   Ⓐ   an honest and open attempt.
   Ⓑ   a sneaky but successful attempt.
   Ⓒ   an obvious and shameless attempt.
   Ⓓ   a well-intentioned but unsuccessful attempt.

5. A school's <u>enrollment</u> is

   Ⓐ   its registration week.
   Ⓑ   the person in charge of registration.
   Ⓒ   the number of teachers and other employees who work there.
   Ⓓ   the number of students who are registered there.

6. To misbehave with <u>impunity</u> is to behave badly

    Ⓐ   on purpose.

    Ⓑ   without being punished.

    Ⓒ   without meaning to.

    Ⓓ   in order to teach someone a lesson.

7. To <u>retort</u> is to answer

    Ⓐ   very politely.

    Ⓑ   in a quick or clever way.

    Ⓒ   slowly and thoughtfully.

    Ⓓ   only "yes" or "no."

8. I'm <u>addicted</u> to that TV show. This means that I

    Ⓐ   never watch that show.

    Ⓑ   can't stand to miss that show when it's on.

    Ⓒ   encourage other people to watch the show.

    Ⓓ   watch it when I'm home but don't really care if I miss it.

9. A three-year <u>stint</u> in the Navy means

    Ⓐ   three years devoted to serving in the Navy.

    Ⓑ   a three-year break from Navy service.

    Ⓒ   three years spent researching the Navy.

    Ⓓ   three years as a Navy captain.

10. To <u>stint</u> on luxuries is to

    Ⓐ   enjoy luxuries very much.

    Ⓑ   limit luxuries.

    Ⓒ   have no luxuries at all.

    Ⓓ   dream of luxuries.

11. Which is an example of <u>intimidation</u>?

    Ⓐ   scaring people into giving up their rights

    Ⓑ   passing laws that limit people's rights

    Ⓒ   passing laws that give people new rights

    Ⓓ   fearing bad weather such as thunderstorms

12. Which is underlined{addictive}?

    Ⓐ   a doctor who treats people with drug habits

    Ⓑ   a person who has a drug habit

    Ⓒ   a drug treatment center

    Ⓓ   a habit-forming drug

13. A popular music underlined{addict} is

    Ⓐ   a store that sells CDs.

    Ⓑ   a musician who records CDs.

    Ⓒ   a person who is enthusiastic about popular music.

    Ⓓ   a photograph of a popular musician.

Find a SYNONYM for each underlined word. Then fill in the circle next to your answer.

14. aspires

    Ⓐ   discovers

    Ⓑ   explores

    Ⓒ   seeks

    Ⓓ   wonders

15. bias

    Ⓐ   explain

    Ⓑ   teach

    Ⓒ   organize

    Ⓓ   influence

16. enroll

    Ⓐ   register

    Ⓑ   succeed

    Ⓒ   attend

    Ⓓ   participate

17. flustered

    Ⓐ   cheered

    Ⓑ   infuriated

    Ⓒ   confused

    Ⓓ   soothed

18. <u>intimidated</u>

     Ⓐ bullied

     Ⓑ requested

     Ⓒ coaxed

     Ⓓ pleaded

19. <u>retort</u>

     Ⓐ comment

     Ⓑ reply

     Ⓒ exclamation

     Ⓓ whisper

20. <u>stint</u>

     Ⓐ stinginess

     Ⓑ unwillingness

     Ⓒ limit

     Ⓓ strictness

21. <u>aspiration</u>

     Ⓐ medication

     Ⓑ treatment

     Ⓒ education

     Ⓓ ambition

Find an ANTONYM for each underlined word. Then fill in the circle next to your answer.

22. <u>biased</u>

     Ⓐ hard-working

     Ⓑ honest

     Ⓒ impartial

     Ⓓ reliable

23. <u>candid</u>

     Ⓐ envious

     Ⓑ stingy

     Ⓒ furious

     Ⓓ secretive

24. <u>intensified</u>

    Ⓐ   faded

    Ⓑ   whispered

    Ⓒ   sickened

    Ⓓ   stumbled

25. <u>obnoxious</u>

    Ⓐ   spicy

    Ⓑ   pleasant

    Ⓒ   intense

    Ⓓ   plain

Find the words that correctly complete each analogy. Then fill in the circle next to your answer.

26. <u>confront</u> : flee ::

    Ⓐ   win : triumph

    Ⓑ   win : outnumber

    Ⓒ   win : fight

    Ⓓ   win : lose

27. finale : last ::

    Ⓐ   <u>debut</u> : first

    Ⓑ   <u>debut</u> : performance

    Ⓒ   <u>debut</u> : second

    Ⓓ   <u>debut</u> : public

28. illiteracy : education ::

    Ⓐ   <u>addiction</u> : drug

    Ⓑ   <u>addiction</u> : treatment

    Ⓒ   <u>addiction</u> : habit-forming

    Ⓓ   <u>addiction</u> : desire

29. get-together : friendly ::

    Ⓐ   <u>confrontation</u> : meeting

    Ⓑ   <u>confrontation</u> : hostile

    Ⓒ   <u>confrontation</u> : pleasant

    Ⓓ   <u>confrontation</u> : peaceful

Book 7, Lesson 7 Test

Choose the BEST way to complete each sentence or answer each question. Then fill in the circle next to your answer.

1. Someone who lies <u>prostrate</u> is

   Ⓐ not telling the truth.

   Ⓑ lying flat.

   Ⓒ curled up in ball.

   Ⓓ on the floor.

2. To <u>gratify</u> someone's request is to

   Ⓐ give that person what he or she asked for.

   Ⓑ ask that person what he or she would like.

   Ⓒ believe that he or she is too greedy.

   Ⓓ ignore his or her request.

3. To <u>pluck</u> an apple is to

   Ⓐ find it delicious.

   Ⓑ give it to someone.

   Ⓒ pick it.

   Ⓓ receive it.

4. To <u>ponder</u> a question is to

   Ⓐ ask it.

   Ⓑ answer it.

   Ⓒ think it over quickly.

   Ⓓ think it over carefully.

5. Where is someone MOST likely to lie <u>prostrate</u> to show respect?

   Ⓐ in a church

   Ⓑ in a court of law

   Ⓒ in the supermarket

   Ⓓ at a baseball game

Find a SYNONYM for each underlined word. Then fill in the circle next to your answer.

6. beseech

    Ⓐ   scream

    Ⓑ   command

    Ⓒ   beg

    Ⓓ   suggest

7. delectable

    Ⓐ   delicious

    Ⓑ   spicy

    Ⓒ   hot

    Ⓓ   juicy

8. garland

    Ⓐ   flower

    Ⓑ   wreath

    Ⓒ   leaf

    Ⓓ   tree

9. gratifying

    Ⓐ   surprising

    Ⓑ   unusual

    Ⓒ   exquisite

    Ⓓ   pleasing

10. impetuous

    Ⓐ   mischievous

    Ⓑ   hasty

    Ⓒ   unfeeling

    Ⓓ   unreasonable

11. lavish

    Ⓐ   gorgeous

    Ⓑ   decorated

    Ⓒ   costly

    Ⓓ   enjoyable

12. privilege

    Ⓐ   wealth

    Ⓑ   advantage

    Ⓒ   beauty

    Ⓓ   generosity

13. rapture

    Ⓐ   imprisonment

    Ⓑ   nervousness

    Ⓒ   curiosity

    Ⓓ   delight

Find an ANTONYM for each underlined word. Then fill in the circle next to your answer.

14. gratified

    Ⓐ   uneducated

    Ⓑ   puzzled

    Ⓒ   frightened

    Ⓓ   disappointed

15. lavish

    Ⓐ   cold

    Ⓑ   inadequate

    Ⓒ   distasteful

    Ⓓ   uncomfortable

16. pluck

    Ⓐ   cowardice

    Ⓑ   malice

    Ⓒ   envy

    Ⓓ   laziness

17. privileged

    Ⓐ   chilly

    Ⓑ   rough

    Ⓒ   dilapidated

    Ⓓ   deprived

18. prostrate

    Ⓐ attractive

    Ⓑ energized

    Ⓒ intelligent

    Ⓓ organized

19. revelry

    Ⓐ daydreaming

    Ⓑ studying

    Ⓒ wondering

    Ⓓ mourning

Find the words that correctly complete each analogy. Then fill in the circle next to your answer.

20. cowardice : courage ::

    Ⓐ haughtiness : silence

    Ⓑ haughtiness : beauty

    Ⓒ haughtiness : smoothness

    Ⓓ haughtiness : humility

21. shear : sheep ::

    Ⓐ pluck : courageous

    Ⓑ pluck : farmer

    Ⓒ pluck : chicken

    Ⓓ pluck : cluck

22. hoarding : miser ::

    Ⓐ lavishing : giving

    Ⓑ lavishing : benefactor

    Ⓒ lavishing : money

    Ⓓ lavishing : generous

23. beat : drum ::

    Ⓐ pluck : fight

    Ⓑ pluck : piano

    Ⓒ pluck : rice

    Ⓓ pluck : harp

24. generous : stingy ::

    Ⓐ   plucky : conceited

    Ⓑ   plucky : courageous

    Ⓒ   plucky : cowardly

    Ⓓ   plucky : hero

25. invention : creative ::

    Ⓐ   whim : fanciful

    Ⓑ   whim : tasty

    Ⓒ   whim : fancy

    Ⓓ   whim : expensive

26. enthusiastic : excited ::

    Ⓐ   haughty : contempt

    Ⓑ   haughty : proud

    Ⓒ   haughty : king

    Ⓓ   haughty : lowly

27. joy : wedding ::

    Ⓐ   consternation : weekday

    Ⓑ   consternation : earthquake

    Ⓒ   consternation : weekend

    Ⓓ   consternation : holiday

Book 7, Lesson 8 Test

Choose the BEST way to complete each sentence or answer each question. Then fill in the circle next to your answer.

1. Nasal <u>congestion</u> usually occurs when someone

   Ⓐ   breathes cool, fresh air.
   Ⓑ   smells a foul odor.
   Ⓒ   smells a lovely fragrance.
   Ⓓ   has a cold or an allergy.

2. A war <u>casualty</u> is a person who is

   Ⓐ   in the armed services.
   Ⓑ   killed or injured in a war.
   Ⓒ   leading an army.
   Ⓓ   fleeing a war-torn country.

3. To <u>cope</u> with a problem is to

   Ⓐ   try unsuccessfully to solve it.
   Ⓑ   manage it successfully.
   Ⓒ   worry about it constantly.
   Ⓓ   forget about it.

4. To <u>initiate</u> a new member is to

   Ⓐ   ask him or her to do a certain task.
   Ⓑ   ask him or her to lead a club or group.
   Ⓒ   accept him or her into a club or group.
   Ⓓ   debate whether he or she may join a club or group.

5. An <u>initiation</u> is a

   Ⓐ   club or group's initials.
   Ⓑ   ceremony to bring in new members.
   Ⓒ   club's annual banquet.
   Ⓓ   building where a club or group meets.

6. Anger <u>smoldered</u> in people's hearts long after the war was over. This means that people

    Ⓐ   stopped feeling angry over time.

    Ⓑ   showed their anger openly, though they did not fight.

    Ⓒ   kept feeling angry, though they did not show it.

    Ⓓ   became sick because of the war.

7. Which is an example of <u>negligence</u>?

    Ⓐ   planning a camping trip

    Ⓑ   cooking over a campfire

    Ⓒ   leaving a campfire burning unattended

    Ⓓ   putting out a forest fire

8. Which is an example of <u>congestion</u> on city streets?

    Ⓐ   a new highway

    Ⓑ   a traffic jam

    Ⓒ   new traffic signals

    Ⓓ   very few pedestrians

Find a SYNONYM for each underlined word. Then fill in the circle next to your answer.

9. <u>impediment</u>

    Ⓐ   stone

    Ⓑ   pedestrian

    Ⓒ   obstacle

    Ⓓ   battle

10. <u>acrid</u>

    Ⓐ   painful

    Ⓑ   angry

    Ⓒ   salty

    Ⓓ   bitter

11. <u>congested</u>

    Ⓐ   relaxed

    Ⓑ   overcrowded

    Ⓒ   noisy

    Ⓓ   undecided

12. <u>impeded</u>

     Ⓐ blocked

     Ⓑ strolled

     Ⓒ dismissed

     Ⓓ harmed

13. <u>initiated</u>

     Ⓐ continued

     Ⓑ started

     Ⓒ explored

     Ⓓ grouped

14. <u>irate</u>

     Ⓐ mournful

     Ⓑ typical

     Ⓒ confused

     Ⓓ furious

15. <u>lax</u>

     Ⓐ scratchy

     Ⓑ smooth

     Ⓒ loose

     Ⓓ long

16. <u>throng</u>

     Ⓐ strap

     Ⓑ crowd

     Ⓒ road

     Ⓓ stadium

17. <u>headlong</u>

     Ⓐ reckless

     Ⓑ tall

     Ⓒ heavy

     Ⓓ mammoth

Find an ANTONYM for each underlined word. Then fill in the circle next to your answer.

18. congested

    Ⓐ comfortable

    Ⓑ well

    Ⓒ clear

    Ⓓ awake

19. inevitable

    Ⓐ manageable

    Ⓑ possible

    Ⓒ enjoyable

    Ⓓ avoidable

20. headlong

    Ⓐ quietly

    Ⓑ kindly

    Ⓒ cautiously

    Ⓓ politely

21. initiation

    Ⓐ welcome

    Ⓑ confusion

    Ⓒ leadership

    Ⓓ conclusion

22. stringent

    Ⓐ satisfied

    Ⓑ generous

    Ⓒ abundant

    Ⓓ relaxed

23. negligent

    Ⓐ pretty

    Ⓑ careful

    Ⓒ tidy

    Ⓓ kind

24. lax

    Ⓐ   strict

    Ⓑ   protective

    Ⓒ   warlike

    Ⓓ   furious

Find the words that correctly complete each analogy. Then fill in the circle next to your answer.

25. sprint : walk ::

    Ⓐ   hurtle : drink

    Ⓑ   hurtle : move

    Ⓒ   hurtle : hear

    Ⓓ   hurtle : speak

26. cheered : applauded ::

    Ⓐ   thronged : yelled

    Ⓑ   thronged : ran

    Ⓒ   thronged : crowded

    Ⓓ   thronged : agitated

27. trickled : poured ::

    Ⓐ   smoldered : fire

    Ⓑ   smoldered : blazed

    Ⓒ   smoldered : fiery

    Ⓓ   smoldered : coal

Book 7, Lesson 9 Test

Choose the BEST way to complete each sentence or answer each question. Then fill in the circle next to your answer.

1. Who are the <u>principals</u> in a conflict?

   Ⓐ all of the people involved

   Ⓑ the main people involved

   Ⓒ friends of the main people involved

   Ⓓ people who are trying to teach important values

2. An <u>era</u> is a certain

   Ⓐ day of the week.

   Ⓑ period in history.

   Ⓒ month of the year.

   Ⓓ time of day.

3. A musical <u>flourish</u> is a

   Ⓐ rhythmic drumbeat.

   Ⓑ quiet, sorrowful tune.

   Ⓒ showy burst of music.

   Ⓓ hit song on the radio.

4. To <u>garrison</u> soldiers is to

   Ⓐ welcome them into the armed forces.

   Ⓑ punish them for breaking rules.

   Ⓒ provide them with supplies.

   Ⓓ provide them with a place to live.

5. To <u>sacrifice</u> is to

   Ⓐ miss someone who has moved away or died.

   Ⓑ give someone a gift on a special occasion.

   Ⓒ buy something that is very expensive.

   Ⓓ give up one thing in order to get another.

6. To <u>flourish</u> your hat is to

   Ⓐ decorate it.

   Ⓑ wave it.

   Ⓒ wear it.

   Ⓓ take it off.

7. To <u>sacrifice</u> an animal is to

   Ⓐ kill it as a religious offering.

   Ⓑ slaughter it for food.

   Ⓒ train it.

   Ⓓ sell it at an auction.

8. The actor bowed with a <u>flourish</u>. He

   Ⓐ moved jerkily.

   Ⓑ made a sweeping motion.

   Ⓒ moved clumsily.

   Ⓓ did a little dance step.

9. The company president was <u>inundated</u> with e-mail messages. This means that she received

   Ⓐ several e-mail messages filled with good wishes.

   Ⓑ a huge number of e-mail messages.

   Ⓒ one or two e-mail messages.

   Ⓓ a few e-mail messages from angry customers.

10. Which is an example of a <u>sacrifice</u>?

   Ⓐ Alicia's parents couldn't afford to send her to college.

   Ⓑ Akiko's mother gave up buying a car so that she could send her to college.

   Ⓒ Geeta's family could not persuade her to go to college.

   Ⓓ Luisa's parents had plenty of money. They could easily afford to send her to college.

11. Suppose a bank loans Mr. Pine some money to buy a car. What is the loan <u>principal</u>?

   Ⓐ the total payment that Mr. Pine makes each month

   Ⓑ the interest that Mr. Pine pays each month

   Ⓒ the amount that Mr. Pine originally borrowed

   Ⓓ the total amount that Mr. Pine has repaid so far

12. Which describes a <u>hoard</u>?

    Ⓐ   a large group of people

    Ⓑ   some nuts that a squirrel has hidden

    Ⓒ   a cave where a bear hibernates

    Ⓓ   a prairie dog town

13. To write with a <u>flourish</u> is to

    Ⓐ   scribble.

    Ⓑ   print neatly.

    Ⓒ   add a fancy line or curve.

    Ⓓ   write in very large letters.

Find a SYNONYM for each underlined word. Then fill in the circle next to your answer.

14. <u>garrison</u>

    Ⓐ   battleship

    Ⓑ   sergeant

    Ⓒ   fort

    Ⓓ   commander

15. <u>dumbfound</u>

    Ⓐ   greet

    Ⓑ   astound

    Ⓒ   capture

    Ⓓ   respect

16. <u>flourish</u>

    Ⓐ   exist

    Ⓑ   glow

    Ⓒ   expand

    Ⓓ   thrive

17. <u>grievous</u>

    Ⓐ   complicated

    Ⓑ   baffling

    Ⓒ   painful

    Ⓓ   extraordinary

18. <u>nomadic</u>

    Ⓐ wandering

    Ⓑ solitary

    Ⓒ welcoming

    Ⓓ rapid

19. <u>principal</u>

    Ⓐ related

    Ⓑ secondary

    Ⓒ primary

    Ⓓ explanatory

20. <u>receded</u>

    Ⓐ exploded

    Ⓑ blared

    Ⓒ sounded

    Ⓓ faded

21. <u>sacrifice</u>

    Ⓐ respect

    Ⓑ bow

    Ⓒ offering

    Ⓓ request

Find an ANTONYM for each underlined word. Then fill in the circle next to your answer.

22. <u>dumbfounded</u>

    Ⓐ amazed

    Ⓑ unimpressed

    Ⓒ exhausted

    Ⓓ worried

23. <u>ensued</u>

    Ⓐ exceeded

    Ⓑ preceded

    Ⓒ escaped

    Ⓓ captured

24. <u>invincible</u>

    Ⓐ speechless

    Ⓑ weightless

    Ⓒ colorless

    Ⓓ powerless

25. <u>placate</u>

    Ⓐ join

    Ⓑ force

    Ⓒ annoy

    Ⓓ interest

26. <u>receded</u>

    Ⓐ parted

    Ⓑ succeeded

    Ⓒ restrained

    Ⓓ advanced

27. <u>ruthless</u>

    Ⓐ merciful

    Ⓑ attractive

    Ⓒ delicious

    Ⓓ warm

28. <u>hoarded</u>

    Ⓐ welcomed

    Ⓑ cured

    Ⓒ spent

    Ⓓ calmed

Find the words that correctly complete each analogy. Then fill in the circle next to your answer.

29. president : company ::

ⓐ <u>principal</u> : leader

ⓑ <u>principal</u> : important

ⓒ <u>principal</u> : school

ⓓ <u>principal</u> : student

30. fill : empty ::

ⓐ <u>inundate</u> : flood

ⓑ <u>inundate</u> : water

ⓒ <u>inundate</u> : drain

ⓓ <u>inundate</u> : valley

31. <u>nomad</u> : tent ::

ⓐ farmer : farmhouse

ⓑ farmer : resident

ⓒ farmer : crops

ⓓ farmer : animals

32. battleship : sailors ::

ⓐ <u>garrison</u> : battles

ⓑ <u>garrison</u> : soldiers

ⓒ <u>garrison</u> : weapons

ⓓ <u>garrison</u> : war

Book 7, Lesson 10 Test

Choose the BEST way to complete each sentence or answer each question. Then fill in the circle next to your answer.

1. To <u>avert</u> your eyes is to

   Ⓐ blink them repeatedly.

   Ⓑ open them.

   Ⓒ shut them.

   Ⓓ turn them away.

2. Someone with a <u>nimble</u> mind is

   Ⓐ clever.

   Ⓑ suspicious.

   Ⓒ lazy.

   Ⓓ disorganized.

3. A person's <u>plight</u> is

   Ⓐ his or her personality.

   Ⓑ his or her family.

   Ⓒ a difficult situation he or she is in.

   Ⓓ a school or college he or she attends.

4. The lion <u>mutilated</u> its prey. It

   Ⓐ hid from its prey.

   Ⓑ chased its prey.

   Ⓒ smelled its prey.

   Ⓓ tore its prey apart.

5. Mona's behavior <u>verges</u> on the ridiculous. This means that she behaves in a manner that is

   Ⓐ absolutely ridiculous.

   Ⓑ not at all ridiculous.

   Ⓒ close to ridiculous.

   Ⓓ unkind.

6. Which is an <u>aquatic</u> sport?

    Ⓐ   baseball

    Ⓑ   swimming

    Ⓒ   gymnastics

    Ⓓ   basketball

7. Which of these would you be most likely to do <u>blithely</u>?

    Ⓐ   study for an important test

    Ⓑ   work out at soccer practice

    Ⓒ   babysit your little brother

    Ⓓ   play Frisbee in the park with friends on a summer day

Find a SYNONYM for each underlined word. Then fill in the circle next to your answer.

8. <u>lethal</u>

    Ⓐ   flawed

    Ⓑ   critical

    Ⓒ   deadly

    Ⓓ   rough

9. <u>assertion</u>

    Ⓐ   response

    Ⓑ   question

    Ⓒ   declaration

    Ⓓ   excuse

10. <u>blithe</u>

    Ⓐ   kind

    Ⓑ   cheerful

    Ⓒ   generous

    Ⓓ   beautiful

11. <u>monitored</u>

    Ⓐ   watched

    Ⓑ   taught

    Ⓒ   scolded

    Ⓓ   criticized

12. <u>verge</u>

 Ⓐ cliff

 Ⓑ beginning

 Ⓒ edge

 Ⓓ ending

13. <u>vigilant</u>

 Ⓐ frightened

 Ⓑ strong

 Ⓒ emotional

 Ⓓ watchful

14. <u>assertive</u>

 Ⓐ interested

 Ⓑ curious

 Ⓒ bold

 Ⓓ angry

Find an ANTONYM for each underlined word. Then fill in the circle next to your answer.

15. <u>blithe</u>

 Ⓐ cautious

 Ⓑ ashamed

 Ⓒ curious

 Ⓓ extraordinary

16. <u>averted</u>

 Ⓐ calmed

 Ⓑ caused

 Ⓒ comforted

 Ⓓ mourned

17. <u>dwindled</u>

 Ⓐ harmed

 Ⓑ released

 Ⓒ pitied

 Ⓓ grew

18. <u>nimble</u>

    Ⓐ   clumsy

    Ⓑ   disobedient

    Ⓒ   disorganized

    Ⓓ   dilapidated

19. <u>docile</u>

    Ⓐ   startling

    Ⓑ   disobedient

    Ⓒ   lazy

    Ⓓ   cranky

20. <u>bleak</u>

    Ⓐ   strenuous

    Ⓑ   reliable

    Ⓒ   hopeful

    Ⓓ   healthy

21. <u>asserted</u>

    Ⓐ   began

    Ⓑ   revealed

    Ⓒ   denied

    Ⓓ   divided

22. <u>bleak</u>

    Ⓐ   violent

    Ⓑ   noisy

    Ⓒ   strong

    Ⓓ   sunny

Find the words that correctly complete each analogy. Then fill in the circle next to your answer.

23. terrestrial : land ::

    Ⓐ   <u>aquatic</u> : mountains

    Ⓑ   <u>aquatic</u> : whale

    Ⓒ   <u>aquatic</u> : water

    Ⓓ   <u>aquatic</u> : sand

24. computer : <u>monitor</u> ::

      Ⓐ   television : VCR

      Ⓑ   television : cable

      Ⓒ   television : channel

      Ⓓ   television : screen

25. swift : antelope ::

      Ⓐ   <u>ponderous</u> : hippo

      Ⓑ   <u>ponderous</u> : cat

      Ⓒ   <u>ponderous</u> : snake

      Ⓓ   <u>ponderous</u> : mouse

Book 7, Midterm Test 1 (Lessons 1–10)

Read the passage. Choose the BEST answer for each sentence or question about an underlined word. Then fill in the circle next to your answer.

THE GILDED AGE

The United States changed dramatically after the Civil War. The war-torn nation became one of the world's economic superpowers. Starting in the late 1800s, fewer and fewer people earned their living by farming and more and more people worked in industry. At the same time, enormous wealth ended up in the hands of a few powerful people. Mark Twain called this <u>era</u> the "Gilded Age." Between 1870 and 1910, millionaires like John D. Rockefeller, Andrew Carnegie, and J. Pierpont Morgan <u>acquired</u> control of many industries. To the <u>consternation</u> of other citizens, these men exerted great influence over the U.S. government. These wealthy men wanted to have free access to public land, have their businesses protected from foreign competition, and be free from government regulation.

These powerful men had many ways of achieving their goals. One thing they did was use their wealth and influence to form monopolies and trusts. A *monopoly* forms when one company controls a certain industry. A *trust* forms when several different corporations have a secret agreement to work together. Companies involved in trusts have <u>devious</u> plans to ruin other companies in the same industry. During the Gilded Age, monopolies and trusts controlled the steel and oil industries. They also controlled the railroads. <u>Ruthless</u> industrialists ran their businesses any way they liked. They did not care who got hurt. The trusts provided the men who controlled them with huge fortunes and <u>lavish</u> lifestyles. This contrasted sharply with the <u>plight</u> of many average Americans.

Bribery was another method of control that was often used during the Gilded Age. In 1872, the Union Pacific Railroad trust made a <u>blatant</u> attempt to bribe the government. The trust sold company stock to several lawmakers for much less than it was actually worth. This bribe was meant to stop the government from taking a close look at <u>negligent</u> building methods. Also in the 1870s, the Southern Pacific Railroad used bribery to maintain a firm grip on California. Senators, judges, and other politicians <u>capitulated</u> to the railroad's power. Southern Pacific held this control until 1911. Another way that businesses worked to get what they wanted was by having their salesmen work for political parties.

At the end of the 1800s, J.P. Morgan bought out Andrew Carnegie and founded U.S. Steel Corporation. This gigantic business was the first billion-dollar corporation ever created. It was clear that the men at the top of these monopolies and trusts had too much <u>authority</u> over the U.S. government. A strong reaction to such unfairness was <u>inevitable</u>.

1. Read this sentence from the passage.

   Mark Twain called this <u>era</u> the "Gilded Age."

   An <u>era</u> is a

   - Ⓐ   certain period in history.
   - Ⓑ   monopoly or trust.
   - Ⓒ   book by Mark Twain.
   - Ⓓ   certain person's age.

2. Read these words from the passage.

   Millionaires . . . <u>acquired</u> control of many industries.

   In this sentence, <u>acquired</u> means

   - Ⓐ   suggested.
   - Ⓑ   did not want.
   - Ⓒ   gained.
   - Ⓓ   shared.

3. Read this sentence from the passage.

   To the <u>consternation</u> of other citizens, these men exerted great influence over the U.S. government.

   According to the passage, how did other citizens feel about the industrialists' great influence over the U.S. government?

   - Ⓐ   They were surprised and happy about it.
   - Ⓑ   They did not care about it.
   - Ⓒ   They were so angry that they were ready to start a war over it.
   - Ⓓ   They were surprised and fearful or unhappy about it.

4. Read this sentence from the passage.

   Companies involved in trusts have <u>devious</u> plans to ruin other companies in the same industry.

   In this sentence, <u>devious</u> means

   - Ⓐ   honest and intelligent.
   - Ⓑ   secret and crafty.
   - Ⓒ   secret and courageous.
   - Ⓓ   difficult and unlikely.

5. Read this sentence from the passage.

Ruthless industrialists ran their businesses any way they liked.

Ruthless people are

- Ⓐ clever.
- Ⓑ generous.
- Ⓒ wealthy.
- Ⓓ merciless.

6. Read this sentence from the passage.

The trusts provided the men who controlled them with huge fortunes and lavish lifestyles.

In this sentence, lavish means

- Ⓐ merry.
- Ⓑ famous.
- Ⓒ costly.
- Ⓓ private.

7. Read this sentence from the passage.

This contrasted sharply with the plight of many average Americans.

A plight is a

- Ⓐ solitary life.
- Ⓑ bank account with very little money in it.
- Ⓒ merry life.
- Ⓓ difficult situation.

8. Read this sentence from the passage.

In 1872, the Union Pacific Railroad trust made a blatant attempt to bribe the government.

A blatant attempt is

- Ⓐ honest and open.
- Ⓑ obvious and offensive.
- Ⓒ secret but well-meaning.
- Ⓓ secret and shameful.

9. Read this sentence from the passage.

This bribe was meant to stop the government from taking a close look at <u>negligent</u> building methods.

Why did the Union Pacific Railroad want to stop the government from taking a close look at their building methods?

    &Ⓐ   They didn't want other companies to find out how to build railroads as well as they did.

    Ⓑ   They didn't want the government to waste its time and the taxpayers' money.

    Ⓒ   They were afraid the government would find out that they were building railroads in a careless way.

    Ⓓ   They were afraid that the government would begin building their own railroad.

10. Read these words from the passage.

. . . politicians <u>capitulated</u> to the railroad's power.

This means that the politicians

    Ⓐ   let the railroad tell them what to do.

    Ⓑ   were surprised by the railroad's power.

    Ⓒ   had more power than the railroad.

    Ⓓ   tried to take the railroad's power away.

11. Read this sentence from the passage.

It was clear that the men at the top of these monopolies and trusts had too much <u>authority</u> over the U.S. government.

In this sentence, <u>authority</u> means

    Ⓐ   expertise.

    Ⓑ   money.

    Ⓒ   power.

    Ⓓ   gold.

12. Read this sentence from the passage.

A strong reaction to such unfairness was <u>inevitable</u>.

This means that

    Ⓐ   there was not going to be a reaction.

    Ⓑ   there was no way to avoid a strong reaction.

    Ⓒ   there was going to be a reaction, but it was going to be weak.

    Ⓓ   it was impossible to tell if there was going to be a reaction.

Book 7, Midterm Test 2 (Lessons 1–10)

Read the passage. Choose the BEST answer for each sentence or question about an underlined word. Then fill in the circle next to your answer.

BUSTING THE TRUSTS

During the period between 1870 and 1910, many politicians refused to <u>monitor</u> the greedy practices of big business. They preferred to be as lax as possible in regulating the free market, and averted their attention from this unfairness. Other lawmakers, however, were <u>aghast</u>. Many saw <u>predatory</u> business practices as unfair to the average American. They vowed to make laws that would limit the power of big business, monopolies, and trusts.

One early remedy was the Interstate Commerce Commission (ICC). Created in 1887, this group's job was to regulate the railroads. Until then, railroads could charge unfair rates with <u>impunity</u>. Many smaller companies depended on railroads to carry freight. Since the railroads could raise rates whenever they pleased, they had all the power. The ICC forced railroads to charge "reasonable and just" rates. The Commission managed to restore order to the competitive railroad industry. For the most part, the railroads did not complain about this regulation.

A more important step was the Sherman Antitrust Act of 1890. This act declared all trusts—secret agreements between companies to reduce competitioin—illegal. Unfortunately, it wasn't strict enough and the punishments given to trusts were not very severe. As a result, the act did little to <u>impede</u> the trusts. When Theodore Roosevelt was president in the early 1900s, the antitrust movement <u>intensified</u>. Roosevelt worked to make politics more open and honest, and wanted more government regulation. One step that Roosevelt's government took was to create the Food and Drug Administration. Part of this agency's job was to clean up the meatpacking industry. Before regulation, many <u>meatpackers</u> were <u>indifferent</u> to cleanliness standards. Rotten meat, doctored with dye and preservatives, often reached the public, spreading disease. The FDA enforced <u>stringent</u> standards. This caused meatpackers to vastly improve their methods.

In 1911, the government took another important "trust-busting" step. It split Standard Oil into 32 separate companies. At first, however, this action failed to <u>disrupt</u> Standard Oil's control of the industry. Separate or not, the 32 companies continued to work as if they were still one. The trust-busting movement was not having as much success as people had hoped.

Thankfully, in 1914, President Wilson signed the Clayton Antitrust Act. This law finally put a stop to trusts that had seemed <u>invincible</u>. The act protected workers by helping trade unions. It was also far stricter than the Sherman Antitrust Act. Wilson also created the Federal Trade Commission in 1914. This group <u>acknowledged</u> the rights of American customers for the first time. Though the monopolies and trusts had <u>flourished</u> for many decades, their day had finally passed. They had become a casualty of Americans' increasing desire for fairness to all.

1. In this passage, <u>monitor</u> means

   Ⓐ   watch closely.

   Ⓑ   purchase.

   Ⓒ   punish.

   Ⓓ   honor.

2. Some lawmakers were <u>aghast</u> at the industrialists' practices. This means that they

   Ⓐ   felt very sad about the practices.

   Ⓑ   were ready to declare war.

   Ⓒ   were shocked by the practices.

   Ⓓ   approved of the practices.

3. <u>Predatory</u> business practices

   Ⓐ   are sloppy but well-meaning.

   Ⓑ   are unfair and harmful to others.

   Ⓒ   are fair but strict.

   Ⓓ   cause businesses to fail.

4. Railroads could charge unfair rates with <u>impunity</u>. This means that they

   Ⓐ   did not charge unfair rates.

   Ⓑ   could get away with charging unfair rates.

   Ⓒ   did not realize that they were charging unfair rates.

   Ⓓ   apologized for charging unfair rates.

5. The Sherman Antitrust Act did little to <u>impede</u> the trusts. This means that the act

   Ⓐ   did not persuade the trusts to vote for Mr. Sherman.

   Ⓑ   did not help the trusts very much.

   Ⓒ   did not really stop the trusts from continuing as usual.

   Ⓓ   was never passed.

6. When the antitrust movement <u>intensified</u>, it

   Ⓐ   grew stronger.

   Ⓑ   came to an end.

   Ⓒ   spread all over the world.

   Ⓓ   persuaded the very wealthy to share their fortune with others.

7. To be <u>indifferent</u> to cleanliness standards is to be

    Ⓐ   extremely worried about cleanliness.

    Ⓑ   one of the people who created the standards.

    Ⓒ   somewhat concerned about cleanliness.

    Ⓓ   unconcerned about such standards.

8. <u>Stringent</u> standards are very

    Ⓐ   strict.

    Ⓑ   detailed.

    Ⓒ   vague.

    Ⓓ   popular.

9. The government was not able at first to <u>disrupt</u> Standard Oil's control over the oil industry. This means that the government could not

    Ⓐ   control the oil industry.

    Ⓑ   divide Standard Oil into many different companies.

    Ⓒ   convince Standard Oil's leaders to quit.

    Ⓓ   weaken Standard Oil's control over the industry.

10. Someone or something that is <u>invincible</u> cannot be

    Ⓐ   convinced.

    Ⓑ   defeated.

    Ⓒ   believed.

    Ⓓ   tolerated.

11. To <u>acknowledge</u> American customers' rights is to

    Ⓐ   fight for them.

    Ⓑ   create them.

    Ⓒ   admit that they exist.

    Ⓓ   limit them.

12. Trusts and monopolies <u>flourished</u> for a long time. This means that they

    Ⓐ   thrived.

    Ⓑ   employed people.

    Ⓒ   stole each other's money.

    Ⓓ   gave big parties.

Book 7, Lesson 11 Test

Choose the BEST way to complete each sentence or answer each question. Then fill in the circle next to your answer.

1. <u>Ballast</u> is heavy material that

   Ⓐ   makes a ship go faster.

   Ⓑ   keeps a ship steady.

   Ⓒ   stops a ship from floating away.

   Ⓓ   works like a sailboat's sail.

2. <u>Buoyancy</u> is the ability to

   Ⓐ   float.

   Ⓑ   walk.

   Ⓒ   bend.

   Ⓓ   jump.

3. A <u>detached</u> home is one that is

   Ⓐ   made of wood.

   Ⓑ   not connected to other buildings.

   Ⓒ   part of a large apartment complex.

   Ⓓ   made of brick.

4. To <u>pique</u> someone's interest is to

   Ⓐ   arouse that person's interest.

   Ⓑ   satisfy that person's interest.

   Ⓒ   praise that person's interest.

   Ⓓ   scold that person for being too interested.

5. A doctor uses a <u>probe</u> to

   Ⓐ   measure a patient's height.

   Ⓑ   write a prescription.

   Ⓒ   examine a wound.

   Ⓓ   measure a patient's weight.

6. Allison <u>realized</u> that it was growing dark. In this sentence, <u>realized</u> means

    Ⓐ   felt worried.

    Ⓑ   felt glad.

    Ⓒ   became aware.

    Ⓓ   felt amazed.

7. If one nation is in another's <u>sphere</u> it means that

    Ⓐ   both nations are equally powerful.

    Ⓑ   both nations are weak.

    Ⓒ   one nation has some power over the other.

    Ⓓ   the two nations share a common government.

8. The flood <u>submerged</u> the town. This means that the flood

    Ⓐ   ruined the town.

    Ⓑ   did not quite reach the town.

    Ⓒ   covered the town with mud.

    Ⓓ   covered the town with water.

9. <u>Ultimate</u> decision-making power is

    Ⓐ   a moderate amount.

    Ⓑ   the greatest possible amount.

    Ⓒ   illegal.

    Ⓓ   unfair.

10. What does the following sentence mean? "Tressy is the <u>ultimate</u> in hair-care products!"

    Ⓐ   "Tressy is the best hair-care product."

    Ⓑ   "Tressy is a new and effective hair-care product."

    Ⓒ   "Tressy is the most economical hair-care product."

    Ⓓ   "Tressy is the most popular hair-care product."

11. Which of these might cause a <u>rupture</u> in a sidewalk?

    Ⓐ   chalk drawings

    Ⓑ   litter such as candy wrappers

    Ⓒ   fallen leaves

    Ⓓ   an earthquake

12. To <u>realize</u> a goal is to

 Ⓐ set a goal for yourself.

 Ⓑ reach your goal.

 Ⓒ hope that your dream will come true.

 Ⓓ work to reach your goal.

13. No one remembers the reason for the two families' <u>rupture</u>. In this sentence, <u>rupture</u> means

 Ⓐ break in friendly relations.

 Ⓑ argument.

 Ⓒ decision.

 Ⓓ first meeting.

Find a SYNONYM for each underlined word. Then fill in the circle next to your answer.

14. <u>eerie</u>

 Ⓐ fascinating

 Ⓑ afraid

 Ⓒ deafening

 Ⓓ strange

15. <u>fathom</u>

 Ⓐ describe

 Ⓑ understand

 Ⓒ express

 Ⓓ explain

16. <u>probed</u>

 Ⓐ prodded

 Ⓑ slapped

 Ⓒ kicked

 Ⓓ waved

17. <u>tedium</u>

 Ⓐ exhaustion

 Ⓑ boredom

 Ⓒ neatness

 Ⓓ length

18. <u>ultimate</u>

    Ⓐ   admirable

    Ⓑ   beloved

    Ⓒ   painful

    Ⓓ   final

19. <u>ruptured</u>

    Ⓐ   rusted

    Ⓑ   widened

    Ⓒ   lengthened

    Ⓓ   split

20. <u>sphere</u>

    Ⓐ   triangle

    Ⓑ   ball

    Ⓒ   cube

    Ⓓ   universe

21. <u>probe</u>

    Ⓐ   crime

    Ⓑ   detective

    Ⓒ   investigation

    Ⓓ   criminal

22. <u>pique</u>

    Ⓐ   dismay

    Ⓑ   resentment

    Ⓒ   sorrow

    Ⓓ   amazement

Find an ANTONYM for each underlined word. Then fill in the circle next to your answer.

23. <u>buoyant</u>

    Ⓐ   organized

    Ⓑ   gloomy

    Ⓒ   stubborn

    Ⓓ   informative

24. detach

- Ⓐ open
- Ⓑ defend
- Ⓒ create
- Ⓓ attach

25. tedious

- Ⓐ beautiful
- Ⓑ silky
- Ⓒ fascinating
- Ⓓ kind

26. unscathed

- Ⓐ frightened
- Ⓑ bothered
- Ⓒ expanded
- Ⓓ destroyed

27. detached

- Ⓐ gentle
- Ⓑ calm
- Ⓒ bored
- Ⓓ involved

Find the words that correctly complete each analogy. Then fill in the circle next to your answer.

28. heavy : sink ::

- Ⓐ buoyant : boat
- Ⓑ buoyant : float
- Ⓒ buoyant : harbor
- Ⓓ buoyant : water

29. stagger : walk ::

- Ⓐ clamber : swim
- Ⓑ clamber : stretch
- Ⓒ clamber : sleep
- Ⓓ clamber : climb

30. rip : tear ::

    Ⓐ   probe : describe

    Ⓑ   probe : examine

    Ⓒ   probe : imagine

    Ⓓ   probe : instruct

31. cylindrical : pipe ::

    Ⓐ   spherical : circle

    Ⓑ   spherical : globe

    Ⓒ   spherical : bat

    Ⓓ   spherical : cube

32. surface : rise ::

    Ⓐ   submerge : sink

    Ⓑ   submerge : roll

    Ⓒ   submerge : swirl

    Ⓓ   submerge : float

33. mile : distance ::

    Ⓐ   fathom : width

    Ⓑ   fathom : length

    Ⓒ   fathom : weight

    Ⓓ   fathom : depth

Book 7, Lesson 12 Test

Choose the BEST way to complete each sentence or answer each question. Then fill in the circle next to your answer.

1. To <u>incline</u> your head is to

   Ⓐ   shake it.
   Ⓑ   turn it suddenly.
   Ⓒ   lay it on a pillow.
   Ⓓ   bow it.

2. A <u>sacred</u> promise is one that is

   Ⓐ   broken.
   Ⓑ   worthy of great respect.
   Ⓒ   given with great reluctance.
   Ⓓ   not sincere.

3. The earth's <u>orbit</u> is

   Ⓐ   its path around the sun.
   Ⓑ   the distance around the equator.
   Ⓒ   the distance between it and the sun.
   Ⓓ   the amount of oxygen in its atmosphere.

4. David is <u>inclined</u> to carelessness. This means that he

   Ⓐ   is usually cautious.
   Ⓑ   is often careless.
   Ⓒ   worries about safety.
   Ⓓ   protects other people's safety.

5. To <u>attribute</u> a piece of music to a composer is to

   Ⓐ   play the piece of music for him or her.
   Ⓑ   tell the composer about the piece of music.
   Ⓒ   compare the piece of music with one that the composer created.
   Ⓓ   say that the composer created the piece of music.

6. Nita and Cato settled their disagreement by <u>compromising</u>. This means that they

    Ⓐ   found a third person to decide who was right.

    Ⓑ   apologized to each other.

    Ⓒ   each gave up something.

    Ⓓ   decided that one of them was completely in the wrong.

7. Danny does not see the <u>necessity</u> for buying new shoes. This means that he does not

    Ⓐ   think he needs to buy new shoes.

    Ⓑ   enjoy shopping for new shoes.

    Ⓒ   have enough money for new shoes.

    Ⓓ   like his old shoes.

8. When might <u>intervention</u> be necessary?

    Ⓐ   when someone needs help

    Ⓑ   on a sunny day

    Ⓒ   when everything is fine

    Ⓓ   during a pleasant discussion

9. Which <u>orbits</u> the earth?

    Ⓐ   Mount Everest, the tallest mountain in the world

    Ⓑ   the Pacific Ocean

    Ⓒ   the moon

    Ⓓ   the South Pole

10. If two people are having an argument, why might a third person <u>intervene</u>?

    Ⓐ   to settle the argument

    Ⓑ   to tell a joke

    Ⓒ   to learn some interesting facts

    Ⓓ   to share an opinion

11. How could someone <u>compromise</u> his or her reputation for honesty?

    Ⓐ   by telling the truth

    Ⓑ   by lying

    Ⓒ   by encouraging friends to tell the truth

    Ⓓ   by discovering that someone else has lied

12. When is <u>arbitration</u> necessary?

     Ⓐ   when a student does not turn in an assignment

     Ⓑ   when people cannot settle their own dispute

     Ⓒ   when someone gives a party

     Ⓓ   when someone is walking home in the dark

13. Which is an <u>abyss</u>?

     Ⓐ   the tallest building in the world

     Ⓑ   the largest creature in the ocean

     Ⓒ   the North Pole

     Ⓓ   the universe

14. Which is an <u>abduction</u>?

     Ⓐ   a kidnapping

     Ⓑ   a car accident

     Ⓒ   a theft

     Ⓓ   a murder

Find a SYNONYM for each underlined word. Then fill in the circle next to your answer.

15. <u>abode</u>

     Ⓐ   building

     Ⓑ   home

     Ⓒ   shack

     Ⓓ   mansion

16. <u>attribute</u>

     Ⓐ   feature

     Ⓑ   personality

     Ⓒ   drawback

     Ⓓ   question

17. <u>compromise</u>

     Ⓐ   feud

     Ⓑ   friendship

     Ⓒ   organization

     Ⓓ   settlement

18. <u>devout</u>

    Ⓐ   loving

    Ⓑ   sincere

    Ⓒ   kind

    Ⓓ   hopeful

19. <u>enlighten</u>

    Ⓐ   exchange

    Ⓑ   inform

    Ⓒ   settle

    Ⓓ   argue

20. <u>inclined</u>

    Ⓐ   sloped

    Ⓑ   zigzagged

    Ⓒ   curved

    Ⓓ   dropped

21. <u>sacred</u>

    Ⓐ   obedient

    Ⓑ   generous

    Ⓒ   holy

    Ⓓ   careful

22. <u>abduct</u>

    Ⓐ   injure

    Ⓑ   rob

    Ⓒ   steal

    Ⓓ   kidnap

Find an ANTONYM for each underlined word. Then fill in the circle next to your answer.

23. <u>necessity</u>

     Ⓐ   joy

     Ⓑ   money

     Ⓒ   luxury

     Ⓓ   annoyance

24. <u>enlightened</u>

     Ⓐ   ignorant

     Ⓑ   bored

     Ⓒ   disobedient

     Ⓓ   lazy

25. <u>distraught</u>

     Ⓐ   gentle

     Ⓑ   calm

     Ⓒ   exhausted

     Ⓓ   religious

26. <u>capricious</u>

     Ⓐ   well-meaning

     Ⓑ   reliable

     Ⓒ   cheerful

     Ⓓ   careful

Find the words that correctly complete each analogy. Then fill in the circle next to your answer.

27. peak : high ::

     Ⓐ   <u>abyss</u> : narrow

     Ⓑ   <u>abyss</u> : deep

     Ⓒ   <u>abyss</u> : irregular

     Ⓓ   <u>abyss</u> : dangerous

28. settle : quarrel ::

     Ⓐ   <u>arbitrate</u> : subject

     Ⓑ   <u>arbitrate</u> : discussion

     Ⓒ   <u>arbitrate</u> : enemy

     Ⓓ   <u>arbitrate</u> : dispute

29. contented : happy ::

    Ⓐ   devout : religious

    Ⓑ   devout : obedient

    Ⓒ   devout : generous

    Ⓓ   devout : considerate

30. tabletop : flat ::

    Ⓐ   incline : deep

    Ⓑ   incline : rocky

    Ⓒ   incline : difficult

    Ⓓ   incline : sloping

Book 7, Lesson 13 Test

Choose the BEST way to complete each sentence or answer each question. Then fill in the circle next to your answer.

1. A story's <u>climax</u> is its

  Ⓐ beginning.

  Ⓑ ending.

  Ⓒ highest point.

  Ⓓ worst part.

2. To <u>endorse</u> a check is to

  Ⓐ pay for a purchase by check.

  Ⓑ receive a check in the mail.

  Ⓒ give someone his or her paycheck.

  Ⓓ sign the back of a check before cashing it.

3. A <u>strait</u> is a narrow body of water that

  Ⓐ connects two larger bodies of water.

  Ⓑ flows into a lake.

  Ⓒ flows down a mountain into a valley.

  Ⓓ flows into a waterfall.

4. A company pays a celebrity to <u>endorse</u> its cereal. This means that the company pays the celebrity to

  Ⓐ help design cereal boxes.

  Ⓑ appear in cereal advertisements.

  Ⓒ figure out how healthy the cereal is.

  Ⓓ help invent a cartoon character to advertise the cereal.

5. My week-long vacation left me feeling <u>zestful</u>. My vacation made me feel

  Ⓐ tired and cranky.

  Ⓑ rested and relaxed.

  Ⓒ sad and lonely.

  Ⓓ joyful and excited.

Find a SYNONYM for each underlined word. Then fill in the circle next to your answer.

6. <u>arduous</u>

    Ⓐ steep

    Ⓑ rocky

    Ⓒ difficult

    Ⓓ long

7. <u>canny</u>

    Ⓐ humorous

    Ⓑ jolly

    Ⓒ wealthy

    Ⓓ shrewd

8. <u>endorse</u>

    Ⓐ describe

    Ⓑ support

    Ⓒ examine

    Ⓓ question

9. <u>exuberance</u>

    Ⓐ fury

    Ⓑ cowardice

    Ⓒ enthusiasm

    Ⓓ contentment

10. <u>kindling</u>

    Ⓐ relatives

    Ⓑ sticks

    Ⓒ decorations

    Ⓓ children

11. <u>lucrative</u>

    Ⓐ thrifty

    Ⓑ businesslike

    Ⓒ comfortable

    Ⓓ profitable

12. mentor

    Ⓐ adviser

    Ⓑ parent

    Ⓒ employer

    Ⓓ worker

13. personable

    Ⓐ vain

    Ⓑ pleasing

    Ⓒ self-confident

    Ⓓ unusual

14. proficient

    Ⓐ elderly

    Ⓑ energetic

    Ⓒ skillful

    Ⓓ interested

15. straits

    Ⓐ pleading

    Ⓑ trouble

    Ⓒ weeping

    Ⓓ luck

16. zest

    Ⓐ excitement

    Ⓑ danger

    Ⓒ challenge

    Ⓓ fear

17. kindled

    Ⓐ explained

    Ⓑ expressed

    Ⓒ organized

    Ⓓ piqued

Find an ANTONYM for each underlined word. Then fill in the circle next to your answer.

18. <u>exuberant</u>

    Ⓐ   obedient

    Ⓑ   cautious

    Ⓒ   organized

    Ⓓ   gloomy

19. <u>intrepid</u>

    Ⓐ   lazy

    Ⓑ   exhausted

    Ⓒ   cowardly

    Ⓓ   disorganized

20. <u>proficiency</u>

    Ⓐ   disobedience

    Ⓑ   inability

    Ⓒ   hunger

    Ⓓ   exhaustion

21. <u>scanty</u>

    Ⓐ   delicious

    Ⓑ   juicy

    Ⓒ   plentiful

    Ⓓ   spicy

Find the words that correctly complete each analogy. Then fill in the circle next to your answer.

22. interest : <u>obsession</u> ::

    Ⓐ   liking : adoration

    Ⓑ   liking : disapproval

    Ⓒ   liking : hobby

    Ⓓ   liking : acquaintance

23. introduce : topic ::

    Ⓐ   <u>kindle</u> : warmth

    Ⓑ   <u>kindle</u> : smoke

    Ⓒ   <u>kindle</u> : water

    Ⓓ   <u>kindle</u> : fire

Book 7, Lesson 14 Test

Choose the BEST way to complete each sentence or answer each question. Then fill in the circle next to your answer.

1. A <u>plausible</u> excuse

   Ⓐ seems true.

   Ⓑ is certainly true.

   Ⓒ is probably untrue.

   Ⓓ is certainly untrue.

2. An <u>alleged</u> criminal is someone who

   Ⓐ has definitely committed a crime.

   Ⓑ has been accused of a crime.

   Ⓒ accuses someone else of a crime.

   Ⓓ is in charge of a criminal court.

3. Pablo had an <u>incredulous</u> look on his face. This showed that he was feeling

   Ⓐ very angry.

   Ⓑ disbelief.

   Ⓒ mildly confused.

   Ⓓ joyful.

4. The United States Congress and the British Parliament are <u>counterparts</u>. This means that Congress and Parliament have

   Ⓐ different roles.

   Ⓑ the same leader.

   Ⓒ similar roles.

   Ⓓ a different number of members.

5. Which is an example of <u>pandering</u>?

   Ⓐ Annie congratulating her brother at his high school graduation

   Ⓑ a game company designing and selling violent video games to young teens

   Ⓒ Vladimir's parents giving him an allowance in exchange for doing chores

   Ⓓ a teacher giving good grades to the students who have earned them

6. Which of these is MOST likely to be found in a <u>menagerie</u>?

    Ⓐ   monkeys

    Ⓑ   violins

    Ⓒ   CDs

    Ⓓ   magazines

Find a SYNONYM for each underlined word. Then fill in the circle next to your answer.

7. <u>dismal</u>

    Ⓐ   complicated

    Ⓑ   irritating

    Ⓒ   eerie

    Ⓓ   depressing

8. <u>enthralled</u>

    Ⓐ   interested

    Ⓑ   puzzled

    Ⓒ   captivated

    Ⓓ   amused

9. <u>incredulous</u>

    Ⓐ   skeptical

    Ⓑ   fabulous

    Ⓒ   fascinating

    Ⓓ   furious

10. <u>legendary</u>

    Ⓐ   courageous

    Ⓑ   generous

    Ⓒ   famous

    Ⓓ   reliable

11. <u>lurk</u>

    Ⓐ   croak

    Ⓑ   prowl

    Ⓒ   creak

    Ⓓ   crawl

12. naive

    Ⓐ   gentle

    Ⓑ   innocent

    Ⓒ   pale

    Ⓓ   soft

13. preposterous

    Ⓐ   unexpected

    Ⓑ   prominent

    Ⓒ   courageous

    Ⓓ   ridiculous

14. incredulity

    Ⓐ   creativity

    Ⓑ   fantasy

    Ⓒ   terror

    Ⓓ   disbelief

Find an ANTONYM for each underlined word. Then fill in the circle next to your answer.

15. allegation

    Ⓐ   question

    Ⓑ   statement

    Ⓒ   fact

    Ⓓ   crime

16. conclusive

    Ⓐ   unconvincing

    Ⓑ   uncomfortable

    Ⓒ   underground

    Ⓓ   courageous

17. dismal

    Ⓐ   sunny

    Ⓑ   dry

    Ⓒ   windy

    Ⓓ   smooth

18. enthralling

- Ⓐ cautious
- Ⓑ arduous
- Ⓒ tedious
- Ⓓ comforting

19. exotic

- Ⓐ ordinary
- Ⓑ healthful
- Ⓒ reliable
- Ⓓ pleasant

20. naive

- Ⓐ dangerous
- Ⓑ reckless
- Ⓒ obedient
- Ⓓ experienced

21. scrupulous

- Ⓐ dishonest
- Ⓑ timid
- Ⓒ comforting
- Ⓓ rural

Find the words that correctly complete each analogy. Then fill in the circle next to your answer.

22. promise : pledge ::

- Ⓐ allege : wonder
- Ⓑ allege : prove
- Ⓒ allege : claim
- Ⓓ allege : excuse

23. fictional : Ramona Quimby ::

- Ⓐ legendary : *Charlotte's Web*
- Ⓑ legendary : Paul Bunyan
- Ⓒ legendary : Peter Rabbit
- Ⓓ legendary : the president of the United States

24. sloppy : careless ::

      Ⓐ   <u>scrupulous</u> : creepy

      Ⓑ   <u>scrupulous</u> : careful

      Ⓒ   <u>scrupulous</u> : unreliable

      Ⓓ   <u>scrupulous</u> : uncertain

Book 7, Lesson 15 Test

Choose the BEST way to complete each sentence or answer each question. Then fill in the circle next to your answer.

1. To speak <u>impromptu</u> is to

    Ⓐ   make a congratulatory speech.

    Ⓑ   give a lecture to a large group.

    Ⓒ   make a political speech.

    Ⓓ   speak without preparation.

2. Someone with a <u>subtle</u> mind

    Ⓐ   suffered a brain injury.

    Ⓑ   has higher than average intelligence.

    Ⓒ   can understand fine shades of meaning.

    Ⓓ   understands only simple ideas.

3. A full <u>complement</u> of trading cards means

    Ⓐ   about one dozen trading cards.

    Ⓑ   about fifty trading cards.

    Ⓒ   the number of cards in a complete set.

    Ⓓ   a few special trading cards.

4. Jaeger's black shoes <u>complemented</u> his fancy outfit. This means that his shoes

    Ⓐ   completed his outfit perfectly.

    Ⓑ   were the best part of his outfit.

    Ⓒ   clashed with the colors he was wearing.

    Ⓓ   were too plain for his outfit.

5. A printer and monitor are two <u>component</u> parts of a computer system.
   This means that a printer and monitor

    Ⓐ   are less important than the other parts of a computer system.

    Ⓑ   help to form a computer system.

    Ⓒ   are separate from a computer system.

    Ⓓ   are always sold together.

6. The smell of the sea <u>conjures</u> up memories of summer. In this sentence, <u>conjures up</u> means

    Ⓐ does a magic trick.

    Ⓑ brings back.

    Ⓒ describes.

    Ⓓ confuses.

7. Please <u>oblige</u> me by keeping quiet for a few minutes. In this sentence, <u>oblige</u> me means

    Ⓐ earn my gratitude.

    Ⓑ calm me down.

    Ⓒ allow me to sleep.

    Ⓓ surprise me.

8. French painters receive <u>emphasis</u> in many modern art books. In this sentence, <u>emphasis</u> means

    Ⓐ special attention.

    Ⓑ excessive praise.

    Ⓒ criticism.

    Ⓓ too little attention.

9. A <u>vocational</u> school's main purpose is to

    Ⓐ give students a chance to meet new people.

    Ⓑ train students for careers.

    Ⓒ teach recreational activities such as boating.

    Ⓓ give students a high school education.

10. The singer <u>obliged</u> her audience with three encores. In this sentence, <u>obliged</u> means

    Ⓐ bored.

    Ⓑ excited.

    Ⓒ repaid.

    Ⓓ granted a favor.

11. Which is the best example of <u>subtlety</u>?

    Ⓐ an apple's red color

    Ⓑ slight sadness in a piece of music

    Ⓒ a baby's soft skin

    Ⓓ the warmth of the sun

12. Which of these could be a <u>complement</u> to a summer cookout?

    Ⓐ   ants

    Ⓑ   a phone call

    Ⓒ   a thunderstorm

    Ⓓ   clear blue sky

Find a SYNONYM for each underlined word. Then fill in the circle next to your answer.

13. <u>component</u>

    Ⓐ   part

    Ⓑ   motor

    Ⓒ   system

    Ⓓ   power

14. <u>emphasized</u>

    Ⓐ   explained

    Ⓑ   mentioned

    Ⓒ   detailed

    Ⓓ   stressed

15. <u>homage</u>

    Ⓐ   attention

    Ⓑ   interest

    Ⓒ   tribute

    Ⓓ   money

16. <u>medley</u>

    Ⓐ   mix

    Ⓑ   item

    Ⓒ   purchase

    Ⓓ   knickknack

17. <u>obliged</u>

    Ⓐ   summoned

    Ⓑ   requested

    Ⓒ   excused

    Ⓓ   required

18. <u>emphatic</u>

    Ⓐ irritable

    Ⓑ forceful

    Ⓒ obnoxious

    Ⓓ courageous

19. <u>pretentious</u>

    Ⓐ showy

    Ⓑ mysterious

    Ⓒ secretive

    Ⓓ elegant

20. <u>vocation</u>

    Ⓐ recreation

    Ⓑ concentration

    Ⓒ exploration

    Ⓓ occupation

21. <u>rustic</u>

    Ⓐ broken

    Ⓑ rough

    Ⓒ rusty

    Ⓓ sloppy

22. <u>warble</u>

    Ⓐ bubble

    Ⓑ wobble

    Ⓒ sing

    Ⓓ dance

Find an ANTONYM for each underlined word. Then fill in the circle next to your answer.

23. <u>impromptu</u>

    Ⓐ dismal

    Ⓑ tardy

    Ⓒ planned

    Ⓓ ordinary

24. lush

    Ⓐ rocky

    Ⓑ barren

    Ⓒ uncomfortable

    Ⓓ impoverished

25. prowess

    Ⓐ tardiness

    Ⓑ disobedience

    Ⓒ laziness

    Ⓓ incompetence

26. rustic

    Ⓐ noisy

    Ⓑ stressful

    Ⓒ urban

    Ⓓ residential

27. subtle

    Ⓐ obvious

    Ⓑ plain

    Ⓒ ordinary

    Ⓓ steady

Find the words that correctly complete each analogy. Then fill in the circle next to your answer.

28. collage : pictures ::

    Ⓐ medley : poems

    Ⓑ medley : songs

    Ⓒ medley : stories

    Ⓓ medley : sculptures

29. inventing : imagination ::

    Ⓐ conjuring : magic

    Ⓑ conjuring : cooking

    Ⓒ conjuring : creativity

    Ⓓ conjuring : talent

30. urban : city ::

    Ⓐ   <u>rustic</u> : simple

    Ⓑ   <u>rustic</u> : farmer

    Ⓒ   <u>rustic</u> : cow

    Ⓓ   <u>rustic</u> : country

Book 7, Lesson 16 Test

Choose the BEST way to complete each sentence or answer each question. Then fill in the circle next to your answer.

1. A <u>maneuver</u> is a

   Ⓐ surprise attack.

   Ⓑ planned military movement.

   Ⓒ retreat that follows a terrible defeat.

   Ⓓ victory celebration.

2. To live off the <u>bounty</u> of the land is to

   Ⓐ receive payments from the government.

   Ⓑ live off nature's gifts.

   Ⓒ make a living as a government worker.

   Ⓓ receive gifts from landowners.

3. To <u>maneuver</u> a helicopter is to

   Ⓐ repair one.

   Ⓑ hear one overhead.

   Ⓒ skillfully move one into place.

   Ⓓ purchase one.

4. Heidi was at her lowest <u>ebb</u>. This means that she was

   Ⓐ at the bottom of the ocean.

   Ⓑ sleeping deeply.

   Ⓒ extremely weak.

   Ⓓ lying on the ground.

5. When mother cats <u>wean</u> their kittens, they

   Ⓐ play with them.

   Ⓑ lick them clean.

   Ⓒ give birth to them.

   Ⓓ get them to stop nursing.

6. Who <u>maneuvers</u> an army?

    Ⓐ   its leaders

    Ⓑ   its enemies

    Ⓒ   all of its soldiers

    Ⓓ   soldiers' families

7. Why might someone <u>insulate</u> a building?

    Ⓐ   to make it taller

    Ⓑ   to make it look newer

    Ⓒ   to keep heat from escaping

    Ⓓ   to keep insects out

8. What do soldiers wear for <u>camouflage</u>?

    Ⓐ   uniforms that blend in with their surroundings

    Ⓑ   white uniforms

    Ⓒ   medals that glitter in the sunlight

    Ⓓ   shiny black boots

9. Which of the following would you find in <u>forage</u>?

    Ⓐ   cheese

    Ⓑ   oats

    Ⓒ   peanut butter

    Ⓓ   milk

10. Ms. Raymer wanted to <u>wean</u> her family off high-fat foods. This means that she wanted

    Ⓐ   to introduce her family to a few new high-fat foods.

    Ⓑ   to get her family to stop eating high-fat foods.

    Ⓒ   to teach her family more about high-fat foods.

    Ⓓ   to warn her family about poisons in high-fat foods.

11. Which of these animals is using <u>camouflage</u> to protect itself?

    Ⓐ   a chameleon changing colors

    Ⓑ   a loudly barking dog

    Ⓒ   a bee stinging a predator

    Ⓓ   a sprinting cheetah

Find a SYNONYM for each underlined word. Then fill in the circle next to your answer.

12. proximity

    Ⓐ companionship

    Ⓑ nearness

    Ⓒ heat

    Ⓓ moisture

13. ebbed

    Ⓐ splashed

    Ⓑ swirled

    Ⓒ receded

    Ⓓ slept

14. harassed

    Ⓐ annoyed

    Ⓑ arrested

    Ⓒ groomed

    Ⓓ hurried

15. lethargy

    Ⓐ disobedience

    Ⓑ laziness

    Ⓒ tardiness

    Ⓓ sorrow

16. maneuver

    Ⓐ trick

    Ⓑ letter

    Ⓒ vacation

    Ⓓ game

17. mottled

    Ⓐ striped

    Ⓑ blotchy

    Ⓒ red

    Ⓓ furious

18. <u>murky</u>

    Ⓐ deep

    Ⓑ slimy

    Ⓒ gloomy

    Ⓓ dangerous

19. <u>sleek</u>

    Ⓐ glossy

    Ⓑ trimmed

    Ⓒ shaggy

    Ⓓ furry

20. <u>bounty</u>

    Ⓐ reward

    Ⓑ hunter

    Ⓒ runner

    Ⓓ promise

Find an ANTONYM for each underlined word. Then fill in the circle next to your answer.

21. <u>bountiful</u>

    Ⓐ slender

    Ⓑ ugly

    Ⓒ scanty

    Ⓓ rough

22. <u>harassed</u>

    Ⓐ brushed

    Ⓑ tidied

    Ⓒ whispered

    Ⓓ comforted

23. <u>lethargic</u>

    Ⓐ obedient

    Ⓑ energetic

    Ⓒ lucky

    Ⓓ joyful

24. sleek

    Ⓐ   brave

    Ⓑ   honest

    Ⓒ   bulky

    Ⓓ   fancy

25. wary

    Ⓐ   comfortable

    Ⓑ   generous

    Ⓒ   ordinary

    Ⓓ   trusting

26. camouflaged

    Ⓐ   revealed

    Ⓑ   explained

    Ⓒ   liberated

    Ⓓ   untangled

27. ebbed

    Ⓐ   displayed

    Ⓑ   rose

    Ⓒ   controlled

    Ⓓ   hurried

28. replenished

    Ⓐ   broke

    Ⓑ   washed

    Ⓒ   emptied

    Ⓓ   hid

Find the words that correctly complete each analogy. Then fill in the circle next to your answer.

29. shopping : peanut butter ::

    Ⓐ   foraging : houses

    Ⓑ   foraging : berries

    Ⓒ   foraging : pajamas

    Ⓓ   foraging : potato chips

30. refrigeration : cold ::

    Ⓐ   <u>insulation</u> : cheerful

    Ⓑ   <u>insulation</u> : well-fed

    Ⓒ   <u>insulation</u> : healthy

    Ⓓ   <u>insulation</u> : warm

Book 7, Lesson 17 Test

Choose the BEST way to complete each sentence or answer each question. Then fill in the circle next to your answer.

1. To <u>appoint</u> a meeting time is to

   Ⓐ set a time for a meeting.
   Ⓑ cancel a meeting.
   Ⓒ look at a clock.
   Ⓓ start a meeting on time.

2. When two people <u>consult</u> with each other, they

   Ⓐ gossip about friends and acquaintances.
   Ⓑ talk things over in order to reach a decision.
   Ⓒ argue with each other over the price of an item.
   Ⓓ debate an unimportant topic.

3. Ms. Boynton <u>resolved</u> to get more exercise. This means that she

   Ⓐ promised herself that she would get more exercise.
   Ⓑ scolded herself for not exercising often enough.
   Ⓒ refused to exercise.
   Ⓓ began to exercise more often.

4. A thumbs-up sign <u>signifies</u> approval. In this sentence, <u>signifies</u> means

   Ⓐ shows.
   Ⓑ questions.
   Ⓒ refuses.
   Ⓓ requests.

5. A <u>significant</u> event is

   Ⓐ an everyday event.
   Ⓑ an important event.
   Ⓒ an amusing event.
   Ⓓ a tragic event.

6. A matter of <u>sovereign</u> importance is

    Ⓐ   unimportant.

    Ⓑ   fairly unimportant.

    Ⓒ   somewhat important.

    Ⓓ   more important than all other matters.

7. A dental <u>appointment</u> is

    Ⓐ   a dentist.

    Ⓑ   an arrangement to meet with a dentist.

    Ⓒ   a dental school.

    Ⓓ   a dentist's office.

8. The Senate rejected the president's <u>appointment</u>. This means that the Senate rejected

    Ⓐ   a law that the president wanted passed.

    Ⓑ   a treaty that the president wanted the United States to sign.

    Ⓒ   a person that the president chose to take a certain job.

    Ⓓ   a plan that the president wanted the Senate to follow.

9. When you <u>consult</u> someone, you are looking for

    Ⓐ   advice.

    Ⓑ   money.

    Ⓒ   gifts.

    Ⓓ   meals.

10. A <u>sovereign</u> nation is

    Ⓐ   rich.

    Ⓑ   independent.

    Ⓒ   filled with natural resources.

    Ⓓ   heavily populated.

Find a SYNONYM for each underlined word. Then fill in the circle next to your answer.

11. <u>assented</u>

    Ⓐ   discussed

    Ⓑ   climbed

    Ⓒ   agreed

    Ⓓ   rose

12. <u>consultant</u>

    Ⓐ advisor

    Ⓑ president

    Ⓒ parent

    Ⓓ teacher

13. <u>flabbergasted</u>

    Ⓐ destroyed

    Ⓑ amazed

    Ⓒ furious

    Ⓓ exhausted

14. <u>procured</u>

    Ⓐ healed

    Ⓑ groomed

    Ⓒ obtained

    Ⓓ forgot

15. <u>resolve</u>

    Ⓐ revolution

    Ⓑ explanation

    Ⓒ question

    Ⓓ intention

16. <u>significance</u>

    Ⓐ greeting

    Ⓑ meaning

    Ⓒ feeling

    Ⓓ impatience

17. <u>sovereign</u>

    Ⓐ monarch

    Ⓑ representative

    Ⓒ lawmaker

    Ⓓ officer

18. signify

    Ⓐ wave

    Ⓑ greet

    Ⓒ show

    Ⓓ rule

19. resolved

    Ⓐ solved

    Ⓑ revolved

    Ⓒ carved

    Ⓓ scrubbed

20. sovereignty

    Ⓐ wealth

    Ⓑ self-government

    Ⓒ peace

    Ⓓ victory

21. haggle

    Ⓐ misbehave

    Ⓑ bargain

    Ⓒ gossip

    Ⓓ mock

Find an ANTONYM for each underlined word. Then fill in the circle next to your answer.

22. assent

    Ⓐ descent

    Ⓑ dive

    Ⓒ interest

    Ⓓ refusal

23. dissuaded

    Ⓐ persuaded

    Ⓑ comforted

    Ⓒ organized

    Ⓓ questioned

24. <u>perturbed</u>

     Ⓐ   revealed

     Ⓑ   soothed

     Ⓒ   answered

     Ⓓ   fascinated

25. <u>receptive</u>

     Ⓐ   disobedient

     Ⓑ   lazy

     Ⓒ   disorganized

     Ⓓ   hostile

26. <u>trifling</u>

     Ⓐ   honest

     Ⓑ   important

     Ⓒ   generous

     Ⓓ   relaxed

27. <u>repudiated</u>

     Ⓐ   accepted

     Ⓑ   divided

     Ⓒ   ignored

     Ⓓ   discovered

28. <u>concur</u>

     Ⓐ   irritate

     Ⓑ   weaken

     Ⓒ   disagree

     Ⓓ   lose

Find the words that correctly complete each analogy. Then fill in the circle next to your answer.

29. president : elected ::

     Ⓐ   Supreme Court justice : <u>appointed</u>

     Ⓑ   chosen : <u>appointed</u>

     Ⓒ   mayor : <u>appointed</u>

     Ⓓ   nation : <u>appointed</u>

30. party : celebration ::

    Ⓐ   <u>consultation</u> : doctor

    Ⓑ   <u>consultation</u> : attorney

    Ⓒ   <u>consultation</u> : meeting

    Ⓓ   <u>consultation</u> : advice

Book 7, Lesson 18 Test

Choose the BEST way to complete each sentence or answer each question. Then fill in the circle next to your answer.

1. <u>Overwhelming</u> sadness is

   Ⓐ   easy to bear.

   Ⓑ   not genuine.

   Ⓒ   very strong.

   Ⓓ   bittersweet.

2. A story's <u>theme</u> is its

   Ⓐ   main characters.

   Ⓑ   setting.

   Ⓒ   author or illustrator.

   Ⓓ   main idea.

3. Someone's <u>perception</u> of a problem is

   Ⓐ   that person's solution.

   Ⓑ   how that person understands the problem.

   Ⓒ   how he or she reacts to the problem.

   Ⓓ   what he or she did to create the problem.

4. A <u>prospective</u> employee is someone an employer

   Ⓐ   hired long ago.

   Ⓑ   just hired.

   Ⓒ   is likely to hire.

   Ⓓ   recently fired.

5. River water <u>overwhelmed</u> our canoe. The water

   Ⓐ   flipped our canoe over.

   Ⓑ   pushed our canoe in a circle.

   Ⓒ   pushed our canoe quickly forward.

   Ⓓ   damaged our canoe.

6. Joni is a relative of the <u>deceased</u>. The <u>deceased</u> is someone who

    Ⓐ   is giving a party.

    Ⓑ   is famous.

    Ⓒ   is critically ill.

    Ⓓ   has recently died.

7. Many European explorers and settlers <u>oppressed</u> the peoples they found living in the Americas. This means that the explorers and settlers

    Ⓐ   could not communicate with Native Americans because they spoke different languages.

    Ⓑ   unjustly used severe force to keep Native Americans down.

    Ⓒ   paid Native Americans to work as laborers.

    Ⓓ   studied Native American customs.

8. Marcy <u>perceived</u> that she was unwelcome in the store. This means that she

    Ⓐ   worried that she might be unwelcome.

    Ⓑ   figured out that she was unwelcome.

    Ⓒ   was unaware that she was unwelcome.

    Ⓓ   asked if she could make a purchase.

9. I felt <u>overwhelmed</u> by Alissa's letter. Her letter

    Ⓐ   touched me deeply.

    Ⓑ   was long and boring.

    Ⓒ   did not reveal what I wanted to know.

    Ⓓ   irritated me.

10. A <u>theme</u> is a melody associated with

    Ⓐ   a dance.

    Ⓑ   a TV show or film.

    Ⓒ   a nursery rhyme.

    Ⓓ   a lullaby.

11. During World War II, Jewish people were forced to live in <u>ghettos</u>. In this sentence, <u>ghettos</u> means

    Ⓐ   certain sections of cities.

    Ⓑ   tents.

    Ⓒ   high-rise apartment buildings.

    Ⓓ   farms.

Find a SYNONYM for each underlined word. Then fill in the circle next to your answer.

12. <u>acclaimed</u>
- Ⓐ divided
- Ⓑ explained
- Ⓒ praised
- Ⓓ described

13. <u>covet</u>
- Ⓐ regret
- Ⓑ envy
- Ⓒ admire
- Ⓓ steal

14. <u>formidable</u>
- Ⓐ intimidating
- Ⓑ intelligent
- Ⓒ experienced
- Ⓓ competent

15. <u>momentous</u>
- Ⓐ occasional
- Ⓑ lighthearted
- Ⓒ significant
- Ⓓ momentary

16. <u>oppressive</u>
- Ⓐ sweltering
- Ⓑ intense
- Ⓒ emotional
- Ⓓ harsh

17. <u>overwhelmed</u>
- Ⓐ defeated
- Ⓑ discovered
- Ⓒ assisted
- Ⓓ shouted

18. <u>perceived</u>

   Ⓐ   received

   Ⓑ   sensed

   Ⓒ   excused

   Ⓓ   persuaded

19. <u>premiere</u>

   Ⓐ   director

   Ⓑ   theater

   Ⓒ   debut

   Ⓓ   success

20. <u>theme</u>

   Ⓐ   poem

   Ⓑ   essay

   Ⓒ   story

   Ⓓ   novel

21. <u>acclaim</u>

   Ⓐ   gossip

   Ⓑ   approval

   Ⓒ   discussion

   Ⓓ   argument

22. <u>bigotry</u>

   Ⓐ   intolerance

   Ⓑ   mischief

   Ⓒ   depression

   Ⓓ   aggression

23. <u>staunch</u>

   Ⓐ   quiet

   Ⓑ   wary

   Ⓒ   usual

   Ⓓ   faithful

Find an ANTONYM for each underlined word. Then fill in the circle next to your answer.

24. <u>coveted</u>

- Ⓐ   unprotected
- Ⓑ   revealed
- Ⓒ   ruined
- Ⓓ   undesirable

25. <u>deceased</u>

- Ⓐ   living
- Ⓑ   exuberant
- Ⓒ   repaired
- Ⓓ   clean

26. <u>formidable</u>

- Ⓐ   cheerful
- Ⓑ   organized
- Ⓒ   easy
- Ⓓ   valuable

27. <u>oppressed</u>

- Ⓐ   widened
- Ⓑ   relieved
- Ⓒ   expanded
- Ⓓ   misinformed

28. <u>spurn</u>

- Ⓐ   hide
- Ⓑ   freeze
- Ⓒ   mix
- Ⓓ   welcome

29. <u>oppression</u>

- Ⓐ   strength
- Ⓑ   understanding
- Ⓒ   freedom
- Ⓓ   health

Find the words that correctly complete the analogy. Then fill in the circle next to your answer.

30. bully : aggressive ::

     Ⓐ   <u>bigot</u> : prejudiced

     Ⓑ   <u>bigot</u> : lazy

     Ⓒ   <u>bigot</u> : mischievous

     Ⓓ   <u>bigot</u> : unreliable

Book 7, Lesson 19 Test

Choose the BEST way to complete each sentence or answer each question. Then fill in the circle next to your answer.

1. To work with <u>dispatch</u> is to work

   Ⓐ   carefully.
   Ⓑ   reluctantly.
   Ⓒ   quickly.
   Ⓓ   for pay.

2. An <u>alternative</u> plan is one that

   Ⓐ   will probably not work.
   Ⓑ   someone might follow instead of the original plan.
   Ⓒ   no one has tried before because it is too risky.
   Ⓓ   is foolproof.

3. To act in an <u>aloof</u> manner is to

   Ⓐ   be cool and unfriendly.
   Ⓑ   be calm and steady.
   Ⓒ   act too quickly.
   Ⓓ   be nervous and irritable.

4. The coach <u>dispatched</u> her assistant on an errand. She

   Ⓐ   went with her assistant to run the errand.
   Ⓑ   sent her assistant off on an errand.
   Ⓒ   could not find her assistant, who was off on an errand.
   Ⓓ   did not trust her assistant to do errands for her.

5. To make a <u>distinction</u> between two groups is to

   Ⓐ   keep them apart for their own good.
   Ⓑ   recognize ways in which they differ.
   Ⓒ   start an argument between them.
   Ⓓ   bring them together to form a larger group.

6. To <u>participate</u> in a school play is to

    Ⓐ   take part in it.

    Ⓑ   buy a ticket for it.

    Ⓒ   criticize it.

    Ⓓ   praise it warmly.

7. Student government <u>participants</u> are students who

    Ⓐ   would rather not be members of student government.

    Ⓑ   have no student government at their school.

    Ⓒ   take part in student government.

    Ⓓ   go to a school that has a student government.

8. Which is an example of <u>fluctuation</u>?

    Ⓐ   rising and falling temperatures

    Ⓑ   an icy winter blizzard

    Ⓒ   three hot summer days in a row

    Ⓓ   a rainy spring

9. Which is an example of three <u>consecutive</u> numbers?

    Ⓐ   2, 4, 6

    Ⓑ   6, 7, 8

    Ⓒ   5, 10, 15

    Ⓓ   9, 7, 5

10. Jill <u>dispatched</u> most of the leftover pizza. She

    Ⓐ   quickly finished most of it.

    Ⓑ   threw most of it away.

    Ⓒ   gave most of it away.

    Ⓓ   saved most of it for later.

11. Which of the following is a member of the <u>canine</u> family?

    Ⓐ   a dog

    Ⓑ   a cat

    Ⓒ   a mouse

    Ⓓ   a horse

Find a SYNONYM for each underlined word. Then fill in the circle next to your answer.

12. <u>alternatives</u>

   Ⓐ jobs

   Ⓑ plans

   Ⓒ projects

   Ⓓ choices

13. <u>desolate</u>

   Ⓐ dark

   Ⓑ deserted

   Ⓒ dirty

   Ⓓ untidy

14. <u>dispatch</u>

   Ⓐ message

   Ⓑ story

   Ⓒ home

   Ⓓ meadow

15. <u>distinction</u>

   Ⓐ fragrance

   Ⓑ honor

   Ⓒ ending

   Ⓓ sound

16. <u>endure</u>

   Ⓐ upset

   Ⓑ fear

   Ⓒ bear

   Ⓓ flee

17. <u>mauled</u>

   Ⓐ scared

   Ⓑ chased

   Ⓒ devoured

   Ⓓ injured

18. alternative

    Ⓐ idea

    Ⓑ plan

    Ⓒ option

    Ⓓ project

19. fluctuated

    Ⓐ changed

    Ⓑ fluttered

    Ⓒ flapped

    Ⓓ exploded

20. endured

    Ⓐ hardened

    Ⓑ lasted

    Ⓒ crumbled

    Ⓓ divided

Find an ANTONYM for each underlined word. Then fill in the circle next to your answer.

21. distinction

    Ⓐ incompetence

    Ⓑ curiosity

    Ⓒ vanity

    Ⓓ dishonesty

22. endurance

    Ⓐ nervousness

    Ⓑ weakness

    Ⓒ hostility

    Ⓓ impatience

23. adverse

    Ⓐ supportive

    Ⓑ usual

    Ⓒ quiet

    Ⓓ expected

24. aloof

    Ⓐ focused

    Ⓑ lowly

    Ⓒ intelligent

    Ⓓ friendly

25. compulsory

    Ⓐ critical

    Ⓑ soothing

    Ⓒ cheap

    Ⓓ optional

26. desolate

    Ⓐ generous

    Ⓑ joyful

    Ⓒ warm

    Ⓓ interested

27. grueling

    Ⓐ restful

    Ⓑ kind

    Ⓒ cheerful

    Ⓓ strong

28. robust

    Ⓐ dishonest

    Ⓑ weak

    Ⓒ disobedient

    Ⓓ sloppy

29. adverse

    Ⓐ lofty

    Ⓑ forgiving

    Ⓒ favorable

    Ⓓ round

Find the words that correctly complete each analogy. Then fill in the circle next to your answer.

30. feline : tiger ::

    Ⓐ   <u>canine</u> : cat

    Ⓑ   <u>canine</u> : bark

    Ⓒ   <u>canine</u> : wolf

    Ⓓ   <u>canine</u> : growl

31. fought : battled ::

    Ⓐ   <u>dispatched</u> : injured

    Ⓑ   <u>dispatched</u> : killed

    Ⓒ   <u>dispatched</u> : threatened

    Ⓓ   <u>dispatched</u> : challenged

Book 7, Lesson 20 Test

Choose the BEST way to complete each sentence or answer each question. Then fill in the circle next to your answer.

1. Too much sugar may be a <u>detriment</u> to good health. This means that sugar

   (A) may improve people's health.

   (B) may harm people's health.

   (C) does not affect people's health.

   (D) is good for most people, but bad for a few.

2. A <u>derelict</u> is

   (A) a police officer.

   (B) a reckless person.

   (C) an alleged criminal.

   (D) a poor, homeless person.

3. To <u>emit</u> an odor is to

   (A) give off an odor.

   (B) smell an odor.

   (C) figure out where an odor is coming from.

   (D) feel sick as a result of smelling a foul odor.

4. A <u>species</u> is a group of plants or animals that

   (A) are similar in some ways.

   (B) are poisonous.

   (C) lived millions of years ago.

   (D) are dying out.

5. To the <u>detriment</u> of his schoolwork, David got little sleep at night. This means that his sleeping habits

   (A) improved his schoolwork.

   (B) did not affect his schoolwork.

   (C) harmed his schoolwork.

   (D) resulted from too much schoolwork.

6. <u>Foster</u> parents care for

    Ⓐ   their own children only.

    Ⓑ   their neighbors' children after school.

    Ⓒ   children who are neither their relatives nor their adopted children.

    Ⓓ   other people's pets when the owners go on vacation.

7. Automobile <u>emissions</u> are

    Ⓐ   fuels that power cars.

    Ⓑ   gases that cars give off.

    Ⓒ   motors that power cars.

    Ⓓ   factories that manufacture cars.

Find a SYNONYM for each underlined word. Then fill in the circle next to your answer.

8. <u>apathetic</u>

    Ⓐ   unsatisfied

    Ⓑ   uninterested

    Ⓒ   uncooperative

    Ⓓ   enviable

9. <u>badgered</u>

    Ⓐ   strengthened

    Ⓑ   burrowed

    Ⓒ   growled

    Ⓓ   pestered

10. <u>compelled</u>

    Ⓐ   propelled

    Ⓑ   schemed

    Ⓒ   forced

    Ⓓ   excelled

11. <u>deluded</u>

    Ⓐ   confused

    Ⓑ   mocked

    Ⓒ   oozed

    Ⓓ   tricked

12. deplored

    Ⓐ explained

    Ⓑ regretted

    Ⓒ wondered

    Ⓓ explored

13. derelict

    Ⓐ colorful

    Ⓑ cheap

    Ⓒ ugly

    Ⓓ dilapidated

14. diversity

    Ⓐ crossroad

    Ⓑ variety

    Ⓒ velocity

    Ⓓ intelligence

15. emitted

    Ⓐ muddled

    Ⓑ admitted

    Ⓒ uttered

    Ⓓ chopped

16. deplorable

    Ⓐ untidy

    Ⓑ wretched

    Ⓒ unusual

    Ⓓ inconvenient

17. toxic

    Ⓐ grumpy

    Ⓑ malicious

    Ⓒ poisonous

    Ⓓ heavy

18. omen

    Ⓐ sign

    Ⓑ greeting

    Ⓒ reward

    Ⓓ deed

19. foster

    Ⓐ encourage

    Ⓑ request

    Ⓒ warn

    Ⓓ command

Find an ANTONYM for each underlined word. Then fill in the circle next to your answer.

20. inanimate

    Ⓐ cheerful

    Ⓑ generous

    Ⓒ speedy

    Ⓓ living

21. incentive

    Ⓐ punishment

    Ⓑ poverty

    Ⓒ ignorance

    Ⓓ discomfort

22. apathy

    Ⓐ forgiveness

    Ⓑ concern

    Ⓒ generosity

    Ⓓ health

23. deplored

    Ⓐ supported

    Ⓑ healed

    Ⓒ revealed

    Ⓓ desired

24. derelict

    Ⓐ cheerful

    Ⓑ scrupulous

    Ⓒ intelligent

    Ⓓ talented

25. detrimental

    Ⓐ tasty

    Ⓑ plentiful

    Ⓒ beneficial

    Ⓓ cautious

26. ominous

    Ⓐ reassuring

    Ⓑ patient

    Ⓒ silent

    Ⓓ narrow

27. diversity

    Ⓐ tolerance

    Ⓑ sorrow

    Ⓒ smoothness

    Ⓓ sameness

Find the words that correctly complete each analogy. Then fill in the circle next to your answer.

28. fact : fiction ::

    Ⓐ reality : delusion

    Ⓑ fantasy : delusion

    Ⓒ disbelief : delusion

    Ⓓ unreal : delusion

29. wolf : den ::

    Ⓐ badger : furry

    Ⓑ badger : burrow

    Ⓒ badger : mammal

    Ⓓ badger : rabbit

Book 7, Final Test 1 (Lessons 1–20)

Read the passage. Choose the BEST answer for each sentence or question about an underlined word. Then fill in the circle next to your answer.

JACKIE ROBINSON, PART 1

Baseball has produced many heroes. Yet many people agree that Jackie Robinson has earned the <u>distinction</u> of being baseball's greatest hero. At a time when <u>bigotry</u> prevented African Americans from playing in the major leagues, Robinson became the first black ballplayer to break the color barrier. Though he faced <u>overwhelming</u> difficulties, Jackie proved that talent and ability mattered most, on the field and off.

Jack Roosevelt Robinson was born in Cairo, Georgia, in 1919. His mother, Mallie, raised Jackie and his four siblings on her own. When Jackie was very young, Mallie moved the family to Pasadena, California, where Jackie grew up. The Robinsons faced discrimination from their neighbors, some of whom called them names and even threw rocks at them. Jackie did not let this get in the way of his dreams, and from an early age he <u>aspired</u> to greatness. After high school, he attended Pasadena Junior College for two years before receiving a full athletic scholarship to the University of California at Los Angeles. There he lettered in four varsity sports: football, basketball, baseball, and track. No other student athlete had ever done that before.

In 1941, Jackie joined the U.S. Army. The military was segregated in those days, with blacks and whites serving in separate groups. Jackie wanted to attend officer candidate school. He met all the requirements, but at first he and some other black soldiers were not allowed to enroll. Eventually, after a struggle, Jackie and the other soldiers were admitted, and he graduated from officer candidate school, served in the Army, and eventually earned the rank of second lieutenant. <u>Deploring</u> the mistreatment of black soldiers in his unit, Robinson protested against racism in the military.

Jackie left the Army in 1944. He launched his baseball career a year later, joining the Kansas City Monarchs in the Negro National League. His excellent playing and professional behavior caught the attention of Branch Rickey, general manager of the Brooklyn Dodgers. Rickey was one of baseball's most <u>astute</u> executives. He signed Robinson to the Dodgers. Knowing that many people wouldn't accept a black major leaguer, Rickey prepared Robinson for the <u>grueling</u> days ahead. He told him, "Many fans may be hostile. We'll be in a tough position. We can win only if we convince the world you're a great ballplayer and a fine gentleman." Jackie <u>resolved</u> to meet the challenge. He spent his first year playing for the Montreal Royals, a minor league team. Jackie led them to a Junior League World Series title. He was ready to play for the Dodgers.

Starting at first base, he made his major league <u>debut</u> with the Dodgers on April 15, 1947. Though he quickly showed his <u>prowess</u> on the field, Jackie still faced bitter resistance. Racist fans <u>harassed</u> him. Even other ballplayers shunned him. Opponents would spit at him and spike him with their shoes. They hoped to drive him out of baseball. Jackie Robinson, however, could not be <u>dissuaded</u> from pursuing his career.

1. Read this sentence from the passage.

   Yet many people agree that Jackie Robinson has earned the <u>distinction</u> of being baseball's greatest hero.

   In this sentence, <u>distinction</u> means

   Ⓐ   description.

   Ⓑ   honor.

   Ⓒ   choice.

   Ⓓ   job.

2. Read this sentence from the passage.

   At a time when <u>bigotry</u> prevented African Americans from playing in the major leagues, Robinson became the first black ballplayer to break the color barrier.

   <u>Bigotry</u> means

   Ⓐ   intolerant, prejudiced behavior.

   Ⓑ   unfair laws.

   Ⓒ   baseball managers.

   Ⓓ   baseball players and fans.

3. Read this sentence from the passage.

   Though he faced <u>overwhelming</u> difficulties, Jackie proved that talent and ability mattered most, on the field and off.

   Jackie faced

   Ⓐ   average difficulties.

   Ⓑ   great difficulties.

   Ⓒ   family difficulties.

   Ⓓ   few difficulties.

4. Read these words from the passage.

   . . . from an early age, he <u>aspired</u> to greatness.

   This means that Jackie

   Ⓐ   was great.

   Ⓑ   admired great people.

   Ⓒ   set out to achieve greatness.

   Ⓓ   was not sure whether he could achieve greatness.

5. Read this sentence from the passage.

   Deploring the mistreatment of black soldiers in his unit, Robinson protested against racism in the military.

   This sentence means that Robinson

   - Ⓐ regretted mistreating black soldiers in his unit.
   - Ⓑ strongly disapproved of those who mistreated black soldiers.
   - Ⓒ secretly watched other officers mistreating black soldiers in his unit.
   - Ⓓ apologized to black soldiers for the mistreatment they received.

6. Read this sentence from the passage.

   Rickey was one of baseball's most astute executives.

   Someone who is astute is

   - Ⓐ sneaky and clever.
   - Ⓑ wealthy and successful.
   - Ⓒ tolerant and open-minded.
   - Ⓓ wise and practical.

7. Read these words from the passage.

   . . . Rickey prepared Robinson for the grueling days ahead.

   In this sentence, grueling means

   - Ⓐ violent.
   - Ⓑ glorious.
   - Ⓒ exhausting.
   - Ⓓ training.

8. Read this sentence from the passage.

   Jackie resolved to meet the challenge.

   This sentence means that Jackie

   - Ⓐ was not sure if he could meet the challenge.
   - Ⓑ promised himself to meet the challenge.
   - Ⓒ promised Branch Rickey to meet the challenge.
   - Ⓓ had to train harder in order to meet the challenge.

9. Read these words from the passage.

   . . . he made his major league debut with the Dodgers on April 15, 1947.

   Jackie Robinson's major league debut was

   - Ⓐ his first paycheck from a major league baseball club.
   - Ⓑ his first time playing in a major league baseball game.
   - Ⓒ the position he played on a major league baseball team.
   - Ⓓ the number on his major league baseball uniform.

10. Read these words from the passage.

Though he quickly showed his <u>prowess</u> on the field...

<u>Prowess</u> means

- Ⓐ excitement.
- Ⓑ good sportsmanship.
- Ⓒ great skill.
- Ⓓ shyness.

11. Read this sentence from the passage.

Racist fans <u>harassed</u> him.

This sentence means that racist fans

- Ⓐ repeatedly troubled and annoyed Jackie Robinson.
- Ⓑ forced Jackie Robinson to stop playing baseball.
- Ⓒ called out Jackie Robinson's name.
- Ⓓ began to like Jackie Robinson even though they were prejudiced against blacks.

12. Read this sentence from the passage.

Jackie Robinson, however, could not be <u>dissuaded</u> from pursuing his career.

<u>Dissuaded</u> means

- Ⓐ discouraged.
- Ⓑ distracted.
- Ⓒ infuriated.
- Ⓓ weakened.

Book 7, Final Test 2 (Lessons 1–20)

Read the passage. Choose the BEST answer for each sentence or question about an underlined word. Then fill in the circle next to your answer.

JACKIE ROBINSON, PART 2

Eventually things grew easier for Jackie Robinson. Manager Branch Rickey continued his staunch support. In 1947, Jackie married Rachel Isum, a nursing student he had met at UCLA. Rachel and their children helped Jackie endure the pressures of breaking baseball's color barrier. In time, Jackie's zest for the game and amazing skill won over his critics.

In 1947, the Dodgers won the National League pennant, and Jackie led the league in stolen bases. That same season, Jackie was named National League rookie of the year. He made twelve home runs, twenty-nine steals, and had a .297 batting average. In 1949, Jackie won the batting title with a .342 average, and the National League named him their most valuable player.

Over ten seasons with the Dodgers, Jackie enthralled baseball fans all over the country. Throngs turned out to see him, and Jackie rarely disappointed them. Robinson was known to be an intimidating opponent because of his skill in stealing bases. During his career he stole home an amazing nineteen times and the Dodgers won six pennants and one World Series. Most importantly, thanks to Jackie, baseball became fully integrated. Countless African American players considered Robinson their role model and mentor.

After retiring from baseball in 1957, Jackie looked for new vocations. He became vice president of a New York coffee and restaurant chain and cofounded a bank in Harlem. He later started a construction company. His goal in his business work was to improve the lives of African Americans, especially those who lived in cities. Jackie also ventured outside of business to star in a movie biography of his life. A friend of Dr. Martin Luther King Jr., Robinson became a leading voice in the Civil Rights movement. In 1964, New York's governor made a special appointment. He made Jackie Robinson his special assistant of community affairs. In 1968, Robinson worked for Vice President Hubert Humphrey's presidential campaign. Robinson worked hard to encourage racial and ethnic diversity in American life and lent a helping hand to a number of church and community organizations. As a result of his legendary heroism on the baseball diamond, he was inducted into the Baseball Hall of Fame in 1962, the first African American to receive that honor. In 1997, the fiftieth anniversary of Jackie's entrance into the major leagues was celebrated by forever retiring his number 42 in a ceremony at Shea Stadium.

Jackie Robinson never compromised his principles. He worked tirelessly for the values he believed in such as human dignity and brotherhood. Sadly, Robinson's life was cut short by diabetes. He died of the disease on October 24, 1972, at the age of 53. In 1973, Rachel

Robinson founded the Jackie Robinson Foundation in her husband's memory. Today this group fosters educational opportunities for minority youth, providing scholarships for college. Jackie Robinson's memory still kindles hope in the hearts of young people everywhere.

1. Staunch support is

    Ⓐ   strong, faithful support.

    Ⓑ   support from a family member.

    Ⓒ   support from the government.

    Ⓓ   financial support.

2. To endure pressures is to

    Ⓐ   cause them.

    Ⓑ   bear them.

    Ⓒ   make them easier to bear.

    Ⓓ   complain about them.

3. Jackie Robinson had zest for baseball. This means that he

    Ⓐ   was a talented ballplayer.

    Ⓑ   was a famous ballplayer.

    Ⓒ   worked hard to stay in shape.

    Ⓓ   enjoyed the game very much.

4. Robinson enthralled his fans. This means that he

    Ⓐ   answered their letters.

    Ⓑ   thrilled them.

    Ⓒ   disappointed them.

    Ⓓ   thanked them.

5. Throngs are

    Ⓐ   fans.

    Ⓑ   baseball scouts.

    Ⓒ   large groups of people.

    Ⓓ   young people who play baseball.

6. Some African American ballplayers considered Jackie Robinson their mentor. A mentor is

    Ⓐ   an adviser.

    Ⓑ   a parent.

    Ⓒ   a baseball coach.

    Ⓓ   a teammate.

7. Jackie had other <u>vocations</u> besides baseball. A <u>vocation</u> is

    Ⓐ   a sport.

    Ⓑ   a recreational pastime.

    Ⓒ   an occupation or job.

    Ⓓ   a dream or goal.

8. In this passage, <u>appointment</u> means

    Ⓐ   the act of choosing someone for a position.

    Ⓑ   the act of setting a time for a meeting.

    Ⓒ   an arrangement or agreement to meet.

    Ⓓ   frustration or sadness.

9. In this passage, <u>legendary</u> means

    Ⓐ   famous.

    Ⓑ   wealthy.

    Ⓒ   exaggerated.

    Ⓓ   unreal.

10. Jackie Robinson never <u>compromised</u> his principles. This means that he

    Ⓐ   never made deals with school officials.

    Ⓑ   always stuck to his own high standards.

    Ⓒ   never criticized others when they behaved badly.

    Ⓓ   never cared what other people thought about him.

11. To <u>foster</u> educational opportunities means to

    Ⓐ   provide shelter for children.

    Ⓑ   study hard in order to get into college.

    Ⓒ   help educational opportunities grow.

    Ⓓ   open a new training camp for young baseball players.

12. To <u>kindle</u> hope in someone's heart is to

    Ⓐ   hope that that person will be all right.

    Ⓑ   get that person ready for a disappointment.

    Ⓒ   treat that person kindly.

    Ⓓ   help that person feel hopeful.

Book 7, Final Test 3 (Lessons 1–20)

Read the passage. Choose the BEST answer for each sentence or question about an underlined word. Then fill in the circle next to your answer.

JANE GOODALL, PART 1

Jane Goodall is one of the world's most <u>acclaimed</u> wildlife scientists. Her <u>pioneering</u> work with African chimpanzees changed the way we look at animals and ourselves. In 1995, the National Geographic Society awarded her its <u>coveted</u> Hubbard Medal "for tirelessly defending the natural world we share." Today Goodall continues to <u>enlighten</u> people about our earth's fragile environment. Goodall shares a message of hope and urges others to <u>participate</u> in environmental protection.

Jane Goodall was born in London, England, on April 3, 1934. She grew up in Bournemouth, England, which is on the southern coast. For her second birthday, she received a lifelike toy chimpanzee. The chimp was named Jubilee after a baby chimp that had been born at the London Zoo. Family friends thought that the toy would scare such a young child, but Jane fell in love with it and still has it in her home today. Maybe it was this beloved toy that first <u>piqued</u> Jane's interest in chimps. As a young girl, her favorite books and stories were about animals. By age eleven, she dreamed of going to Africa to study wildlife. In those days, most parents would not have been <u>receptive</u> to such an idea. At that time, young girls were supposed to dream of marriage, not scientific studies. Jane's mother was different. She encouraged Jane to <u>realize</u> her goal through hard work.

Jane was not afraid of hard work. She first went to secretarial school and then worked for a documentary film company. Eventually, a friend invited her to Kenya. To save money for the fare, Jane worked as a waitress and by the age of 23 had saved enough to make the journey to Africa by boat. When she arrived in Africa, she contacted famous anthropologist Louis Leakey. Leakey was so impressed with Jane's knowledge about Africa and animals that he hired her to be his assistant. Jane worked with Leakey and his wife Mary at Olduvai Gorge in Kenya, where they studied fossils.

Jane enjoyed her work at Olduvai Gorge, but she wanted to study live animals. Dr. Leakey approached her about studying wild chimpanzees on the shores of Lake Tanganyika. Jane was thrilled at the idea. At first the local authorities at the lake were <u>incredulous</u>. They resisted the idea of a <u>naive</u> young woman living among wild animals. But once they <u>perceived</u> how capable she was, they agreed to let Jane begin her study. In July 1960, the <u>intrepid</u> 26-year-old arrived at Gombe National Park in Tanganyika—now Tanzania. (In Part 2 you will learn what she discovered there.)

1. Read this sentence from the passage.

   Jane Goodall is one of the world's most <u>acclaimed</u> wildlife scientists.

   In this sentence, <u>acclaimed</u> means

       Ⓐ   skilled.

       Ⓑ   fascinating.

       Ⓒ   praised.

       Ⓓ   famous.

2. Read this sentence from the passage.

   Her <u>pioneering</u> work with African chimpanzees changed the way we look at animals and ourselves.

   In this sentence, <u>pioneering</u> means

       Ⓐ   courageous.

       Ⓑ   opening the way for others.

       Ⓒ   brilliant.

       Ⓓ   sharing knowledge with others.

3. Read these words from the passage.

   The National Geographic Society awarded her its <u>coveted</u> Hubbard Medal . . .

   In this sentence, <u>coveted</u> means

       Ⓐ   prized.

       Ⓑ   costly.

       Ⓒ   annual.

       Ⓓ   silver.

4. Read this sentence from the passage.

   Today Goodall continues to <u>enlighten</u> people about our earth's fragile environment.

   In this sentence, <u>enlighten</u> means

       Ⓐ   praise.

       Ⓑ   ask.

       Ⓒ   scold.

       Ⓓ   teach.

5. Read these words from the passage.

   Goodall . . . urges others to <u>participate</u> in environmental protection.

   This means that Goodall urges others to

       Ⓐ   help protect the environment.

       Ⓑ   lead environmental protection groups.

       Ⓒ   give lectures on environmental protection.

       Ⓓ   discuss environmental protection.

6. Read this sentence from the passage.

   Maybe it was this beloved toy that first <u>piqued</u> Jane's interest in chimps.

   To <u>pique</u> someone's interest is to

        Ⓐ   find out whether he or she is interested.

        Ⓑ   excite or arouse that person's interest.

        Ⓒ   tell him or her some interesting news.

        Ⓓ   think he or she has an interesting personality.

7. Read this sentence from the passage.

   In those days, most parents would not have been <u>receptive</u> to such an idea.

   This means that most parents would not have been

        Ⓐ   willing and able to consider such an idea.

        Ⓑ   able to understand the idea.

        Ⓒ   able to refuse the idea.

        Ⓓ   able to pay for the idea.

8. Read this sentence from the passage.

   She encouraged Jane to <u>realize</u> her goal through hard work.

   In this sentence, <u>realize</u> means

        Ⓐ   dream about.

        Ⓑ   set.

        Ⓒ   make happen.

        Ⓓ   discover.

9. **Read thi**s sentence from the passage.

   At first the local authorities at the lake were <u>incredulous</u>.

   This means that the authorities were

        Ⓐ   incredible.

        Ⓑ   skeptical.

        Ⓒ   not very helpful.

        Ⓓ   angry.

10. Read this sentence from the passage.

    They resisted the idea of a <u>naive</u> young woman living among wild animals.

    In this sentence, <u>naive</u> means

         Ⓐ   inexperienced.

         Ⓑ   beautiful.

         Ⓒ   frail.

         Ⓓ   silly.

11. Read this sentence from the passage.

But once they <u>perceived</u> how capable she was, they agreed to let Jane begin her study.

In this sentence, <u>perceived</u> means

Ⓐ explained.

Ⓑ learned from others.

Ⓒ asked.

Ⓓ figured out.

12. Read this sentence from the passage.

In July 1960, the <u>intrepid</u> 26-year-old arrived at Gombe National Park in Tanganyika—now Tanzania.

In this sentence, <u>intrepid</u> means

Ⓐ experienced.

Ⓑ skilled.

Ⓒ excited.

Ⓓ courageous.

Book 7, Final Test 4 (Lessons 1–20)

Read the passage. Choose the BEST answer for each sentence or question about an underlined word. Circle the letter of your answer.

JANE GOODALL, PART 2

At first, studying wild chimps was an <u>arduous</u> task. Jane Goodall lived under <u>adverse</u> conditions in a rugged mountain rain forest. The animals fled from her in fear, but she continued to go out in the forest every day to observe them. It took months to gain close <u>proximity</u> to the chimps. On most days Jane observed them through binoculars, watching them <u>forage</u> for food. The work could be frustrating and <u>tedious</u>, but gradually the chimps got used to Jane's presence.

Goodall <u>probed</u> many aspects of chimpanzee behavior at Gombe. She got to know many different individual animals and discovered that each chimp has its own personality traits and habits. She observed chimps making tools that they used to "fish" for termites. This discovery proved <u>conclusively</u> that humans are not the only tool-making animals. Because of Goodall's research, we now know that wild chimps are <u>proficient</u> toolmakers and hunt for meat. Jane's research demonstrated that chimpanzees are more like humans than anyone had thought. The Gombe project is still underway and remains the longest ongoing field study of any animal <u>species</u> in natural surroundings. The project has lasted for more than forty years. Most of the work is now done by Tanzanian people, and the Tanzanian government is very proud of their work.

In time, Jane saw the <u>necessity</u> of taking her message to a wider audience. In 1977, she founded the Jane Goodall Institute. The Institute's mission is to promote education, help save the <u>dwindling</u> population of wild chimps, and improve the global environment for wildlife. Jane has written many books and received numerous awards. She gives lectures to audiences around the world, inspiring them to help save our environment. She still visits Gombe, although she does not get to spend as much time there as she would like. Her favorite kind of day at Gombe is spent following a mother chimp and her babies. Jane will follow the chimps from when they wake up in the morning until they go to bed at sunset. She clambers through the forest to follow them wherever they may go. She often has to crawl though vines on her stomach and when she is out in the field, she eats some of the same fruits as the chimps do, although not all of them taste good to humans. The work is difficult, but the forest is so beautiful and peaceful that Jane doesn't mind. When she is not in Gombe, Jane spends her days traveling, lobbying, writing letters, and educating people about the Institute. She answers as many letters personally as she can. Jane Goodall feels that it is her <u>sacred</u> duty to help make the world a better place. There is no doubt that she has done so.

1. An arduous task

    Ⓐ   is one that someone does for pay.

    Ⓑ   is very difficult.

    Ⓒ   is enjoyable.

    Ⓓ   takes many years.

2. Adverse conditions are

    Ⓐ   unfavorable.

    Ⓑ   rainy.

    Ⓒ   unfair.

    Ⓓ   unbelievable.

3. To gain close proximity to chimpanzees is to

    Ⓐ   become friends with them.

    Ⓑ   get close to them.

    Ⓒ   find out what they are like.

    Ⓓ   read about them in books.

4. To forage for food is to

    Ⓐ   ask for it.

    Ⓑ   grow it.

    Ⓒ   do tricks for it.

    Ⓓ   search for it.

5. Tedious work is

    Ⓐ   difficult.

    Ⓑ   well paid.

    Ⓒ   boring.

    Ⓓ   easy but time-consuming.

6. To probe aspects of chimp behavior is to

    Ⓐ   examine them carefully.

    Ⓑ   discuss them.

    Ⓒ   write books about them.

    Ⓓ   photograph them.

7. In this passage, <u>conclusively</u> means

    Ⓐ   enthusiastically.

    Ⓑ   hesitantly.

    Ⓒ   convincingly.

    Ⓓ   emphatically.

8. <u>Proficient</u> toolmakers

    Ⓐ   are wild animals.

    Ⓑ   are humans.

    Ⓒ   make useless tools.

    Ⓓ   are skilled.

9. Animals in the same <u>species</u>

    Ⓐ   are chimpanzees.

    Ⓑ   are apes.

    Ⓒ   have many traits in common.

    Ⓓ   live in the same place.

10. To see the <u>necessity</u> for something is to

    Ⓐ   realize that it needs to be done.

    Ⓑ   provide food and shelter for it.

    Ⓒ   wonder whether it needs to be done.

    Ⓓ   provide money for it.

11. Chimp populations are <u>dwindling</u>. This means that

    Ⓐ   chimps are extinct.

    Ⓑ   there are fewer chimps than before.

    Ⓒ   chimps are growing weaker.

    Ⓓ   disease is killing many chimps.

12. In this passage, <u>sacred</u> means

    Ⓐ   holy.

    Ⓑ   honorable.

    Ⓒ   difficult.

    Ⓓ   unusual.

<u>Answer Key</u>

Lesson 1 Test

1. A
2. B
3. C
4. B
5. D
6. A
7. B
8. A
9. D
10. B
11. A
12. A
13. B
14. A
15. B
16. D
17. B
18. D
19. C
20. D
21. A
22. C
23. C
24. D
25. B
26. C
27. D
28. D
29. B

Lesson 2 Test

1. C
2. A
3. B
4. C
5. A
6. A
7. D
8. A
9. D
10. C
11. A
12. C
13. C
14. B
15. C
16. D
17. C
18. D
19. B
20. C
21. D
22. B
23. C
24. A
25. B
26. A
27. A
28. C

Answer Key

Lesson 3 Test		Lesson 4 Test	
1.	C	1.	B
2.	C	2.	C
3.	B	3.	A
4.	D	4.	B
5.	C	5.	A
6.	B	6.	B
7.	C	7.	B
8.	D	8.	B
9.	A	9.	C
10.	D	10.	B
11.	B	11.	C
12.	A	12.	A
13.	A	13.	D
14.	D	14.	C
15.	A	15.	D
16.	C	16.	C
17.	B	17.	D
18.	D	18.	B
19.	B	19.	D
20.	A	20.	C
21.	C	21.	B
22.	D	22.	C
23.	B	23.	A
24.	D	24.	B
25.	D	25.	A
26.	C	26.	C
27.	D	27.	C
28.	B	28.	B
29.	C	29.	D

Answer Key

Lesson 5 Test

1. A
2. D
3. C
4. C
5. A
6. B
7. B
8. A
9. D
10. B
11. A
12. A
13. A
14. D
15. C
16. A
17. C
18. A
19. C
20. D
21. D
22. B
23. C
24. D
25. A
26. B
27. D
28. B
29. C

Lesson 6 Test

1. B
2. D
3. B
4. C
5. D
6. B
7. B
8. B
9. A
10. B
11. A
12. D
13. C
14. C
15. D
16. A
17. C
18. A
19. B
20. C
21. D
22. C
23. D
24. A
25. B
26. D
27. A
28. B
29. B

Answer Key

Lesson 7 Test

1. B
2. A
3. C
4. D
5. A
6. C
7. A
8. B
9. D
10. B
11. C
12. B
13. D
14. D
15. B
16. A
17. D
18. B
19. D
20. D
21. C
22. B
23. D
24. C
25. A
26. B
27. B

Lesson 8 Test

1. D
2. B
3. B
4. C
5. B
6. C
7. C
8. B
9. C
10. D
11. B
12. A
13. B
14. D
15. C
16. B
17. A
18. C
19. D
20. C
21. D
22. D
23. B
24. A
25. B
26. C
27. B

Answer Key

Lesson 9 Test

1. B
2. B
3. C
4. D
5. D
6. B
7. A
8. B
9. B
10. B
11. C
12. B
13. C
14. C
15. B
16. D
17. C
18. A
19. C
20. D
21. C
22. B
23. B
24. D
25. C
26. D
27. A
28. C
29. C
30. C
31. A
32. B

Lesson 10 Test

1. D
2. A
3. C
4. D
5. C
6. B
7. D
8. C
9. C
10. B
11. A
12. C
13. D
14. C
15. A
16. B
17. D
18. A
19. B
20. C
21. C
22. D
23. C
24. D
25. A

Midterm Test 1
(Lessons 1–10)

1. A
2. C
3. D
4. B
5. D
6. C
7. D
8. B
9. C
10. A
11. C
12. B

Answer Key

Midterm Test 2
(Lessons 1–10)

1. A
2. C
3. B
4. B
5. C
6. A
7. D
8. A
9. D
10. B
11. C
12. A

Lesson 11 Test

1. B
2. A
3. B
4. A
5. C
6. C
7. C
8. D
9. B
10. A
11. D
12. B
13. A
14. D
15. B
16. A
17. B
18. D
19. D
20. B
21. C
22. B
23. B
24. D
25. C
26. D
27. D
28. B
29. D
30. B
31. B
32. A
33. D

Lesson 12 Test

1. D
2. B
3. A
4. B
5. D
6. C
7. A
8. A
9. C
10. A
11. B
12. B
13. D
14. A
15. B
16. A
17. D
18. B
19. B
20. A
21. C
22. D
23. C
24. A
25. B
26. B
27. B
28. D
29. A
30. D

Answer Key

Lesson 13 Test

1. C
2. D
3. A
4. B
5. D
6. C
7. D
8. B
9. C
10. B
11. D
12. A
13. B
14. C
15. B
16. A
17. D
18. D
19. C
20. B
21. C
22. A
23. D

Lesson 14 Test

1. A
2. B
3. B
4. C
5. B
6. A
7. D
8. C
9. A
10. C
11. B
12. B
13. D
14. D
15. C
16. A
17. A
18. C
19. A
20. D
21. A
22. C
23. B
24. B

Answer Key

Lesson 15 Test

1. D
2. C
3. C
4. A
5. B
6. B
7. A
8. A
9. B
10. D
11. B
12. D
13. A
14. D
15. C
16. A
17. D
18. B
19. A
20. D
21. B
22. C
23. C
24. B
25. D
26. C
27. A
28. B
29. A
30. D

Lesson 16 Test

1. B
2. B
3. C
4. C
5. D
6. A
7. C
8. A
9. B
10. B
11. A
12. B
13. C
14. A
15. B
16. A
17. B
18. C
19. A
20. A
21. C
22. D
23. B
24. C
25. D
26. A
27. B
28. C
29. B
30. D

Answer Key

Lesson 17 Test

1. A
2. B
3. A
4. A
5. B
6. D
7. B
8. C
9. A
10. B
11. C
12. A
13. B
14. C
15. D
16. B
17. A
18. C
19. A
20. B
21. B
22. D
23. A
24. B
25. D
26. B
27. A
28. C
29. A
30. C

Lesson 18 Test

1. C
2. D
3. B
4. C
5. A
6. D
7. B
8. B
9. A
10. B
11. A
12. C
13. B
14. A
15. C
16. D
17. A
18. B
19. C
20. B
21. B
22. A
23. D
24. D
25. A
26. C
27. B
28. D
29. C
30. A

Answer Key

Lesson 19 Test	Lesson 20 Test
1. C	1. B
2. B	2. D
3. A	3. A
4. B	4. A
5. B	5. C
6. A	6. C
7. C	7. B
8. A	8. B
9. B	9. D
10. A	10. C
11. A	11. D
12. D	12. B
13. B	13. D
14. A	14. B
15. B	15. C
16. C	16. B
17. D	17. C
18. C	18. A
19. A	19. A
20. B	20. D
21. A	21. A
22. B	22. B
23. A	23. A
24. D	24. B
25. D	25. C
26. B	26. A
27. A	27. D
28. B	28. A
29. C	29. B
30. C	
31. B	

Answer Key

Final Test 1
(Lessons 1–20)

1. B
2. A
3. B
4. C
5. B
6. D
7. C
8. B
9. B
10. C
11. A
12. A

Final Test 2
(Lessons 1–20)

1. A
2. B
3. D
4. B
5. C
6. A
7. C
8. A
9. A
10. B
11. C
12. D

Answer Key

Final Test 3
(Lessons 1–20)

1. C
2. B
3. A
4. D
5. A
6. B
7. A
8. C
9. B
10. A
11. D
12. D

Final Test 4
(Lessons 1–20)

1. B
2. A
3. B
4. D
5. C
6. A
7. C
8. D
9. C
10. A
11. B
12. B